Veritas Press

A
PHONICS
MUSEUM

MARLIN & LAURIE DETWEILER
DIANE COLEMAN
NED BUSTARD
EMILY FISCHER
ERIC VANDERHOOF

Second Edition 2001

Copyright © 2001 Veritas Press
1250 Belle Mead Drive
Lancaster, PA 17601
(800) 922-5084
ISBN 1-930710-61-5

Printed in the United States of America.

REVIEW

INSTRUCTIONS
After reading *The Alphabet Quest,* write the beginning letter for each museum picture below.

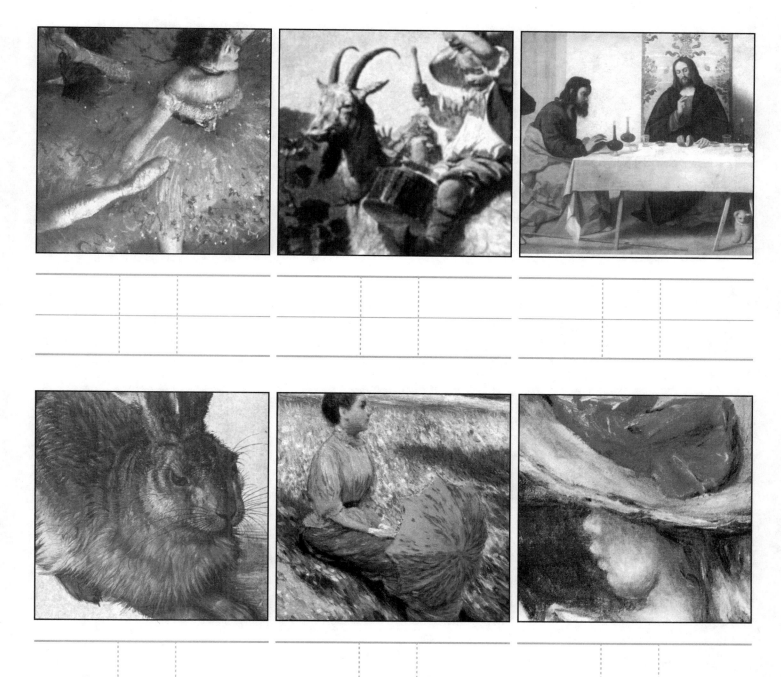

REVIEW

Name

INSTRUCTIONS

After reading *The Alphabet Quest,* write the
beginning letter for each museum picture below.

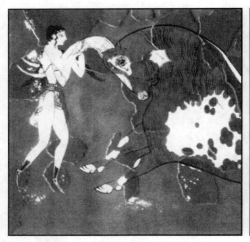

REVIEW

Name

INSTRUCTIONS:
Follow the mazes for each lower case letter, then write its matching upper case letter next to it on the left.

REVIEW

INSTRUCTIONS:
After looking at each picture say its name. Write the letter
for the beginning sound in each picture.

Name

REVIEW

After looking at each picture say its name. Write the letter for the beginning sound in each picture.

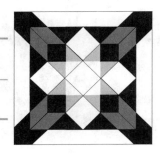

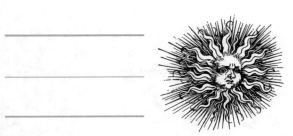

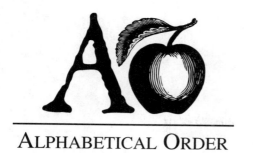

ALPHABETICAL ORDER

Name

INSTRUCTIONS:
Complete the picture by connecting the dots in alphabetical order.

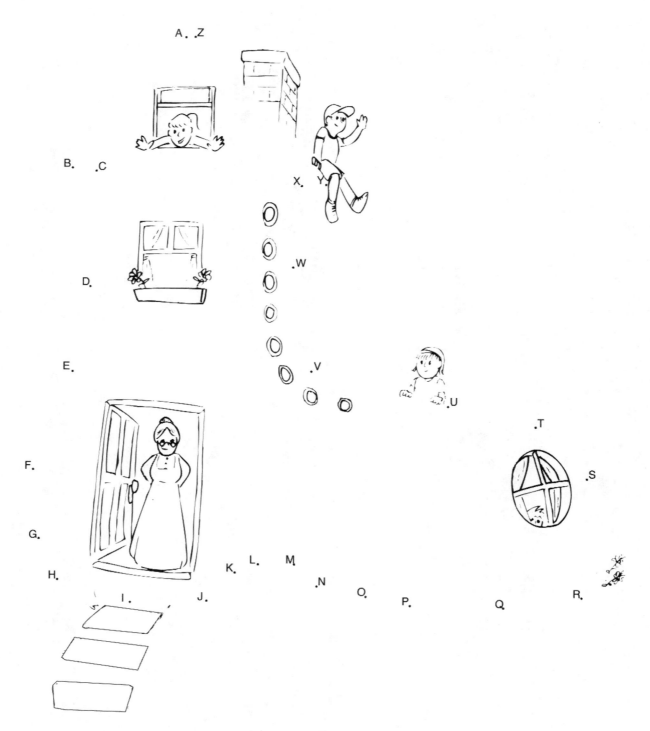

Name

REVIEW

INSTRUCTIONS:
Write the correct middle vowel in each word and follow the mazes for the rest of the word's letters.

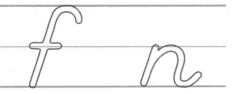

n   t   f   n   b   ll

h   t   d   g   p   g

REVIEW

INSTRUCTIONS:
Read each sentence. Match the correct picture to each sentence.

The lad had
a pen.

The man sat.

The pigs
were fed.

The fat cat
sat.

REVIEW

Name

Circle the letter pair which makes the beginning sound for
each picture.

sh	wh

ch	th

sh	wh

ch	th

sh	wh

ch	th

sh	wh
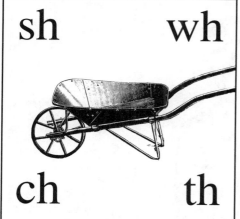	
ch	th

sh	wh

ch	th

sh	wh

ch	th

sh	wh

ch	th

sh	wh

ch	th

sh	wh

ch	th

REVIEW

Name

INSTRUCTIONS:
Write your first and last names on the lines below.

Name

INSTRUCTIONS:
Using magazines, cut out an image for each letter to add to your museum.

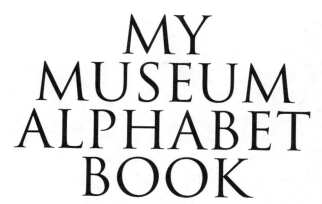

MY
MUSEUM
ALPHABET
BOOK

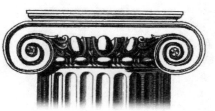

Y

B

REVIEW

Name

INSTRUCTIONS:
Using magazines, cut out an image for each letter to add to your museum.

A

Z

C

X

REVIEW

INSTRUCTIONS:
Using magazines, cut out an image for each letter to add to your museum.

REVIEW

Name

I NSTRUCTIONS:
Using magazines, cut out an image for each letter to add to your museum.

E

V

G

T

REVIEW

Name

INSTRUCTIONS:
Using magazines, cut out an image for each letter to add to your museum.

S

H

Q

J

Name

INSTRUCTIONS:
Using magazines, cut out an image for each letter to add to your museum.

I

R

K

P

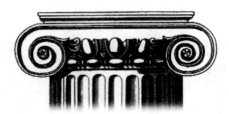

REVIEW

INSTRUCTIONS:
Using magazines, cut out an image for each letter to add to your museum.

INSTRUCTIONS:
Using magazines, cut out an image for each letter to add to your museum.

M

N

ing/ang/ong

Name

Worksheet 6A
Seeing

INSTRUCTIONS:
Circle the "ing," "ang," or "ong" in the following words.

king	rang	song
ring	sang	gong
sing	bang	dong
wing	hang	pong
ding	gang	long

ing/ang /ong

Name

INSTRUCTIONS:
Read the words below.

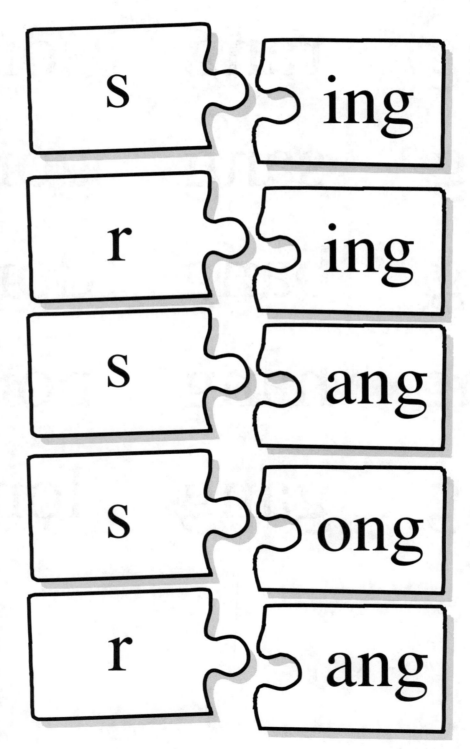

ing/ang/ong

Name

Worksheet 7A
Seeing

INSTRUCTIONS:
Circle the "ing" in the following words.

hopping humming

huffing winning

singing begging

budding

ing/ang /ong

INSTRUCTIONS:
Cut the scroll and the letter strip out then place the strip through the scroll and read the words that are made.

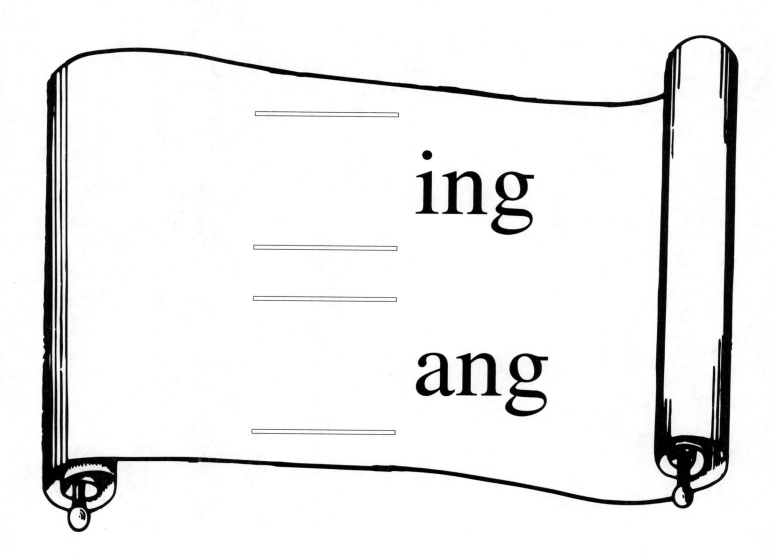

ing

ang

s   r   p   b

ing/ang /ong

Name

INSTRUCTIONS:
Read up and down the word columns. After this you will be able to read *Ella Sings Jazz*.

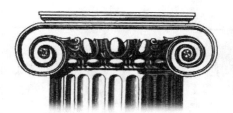  

sing	pong	napping
king	lungs	getting
swing	sung	buzzing
bing	singing	begging
ping	hopping	itching
sang	huffing	budding
gang	puffing	humming
bang	dipping	zinging
songs	rocking	like
long	swinging	loving

REVIEW

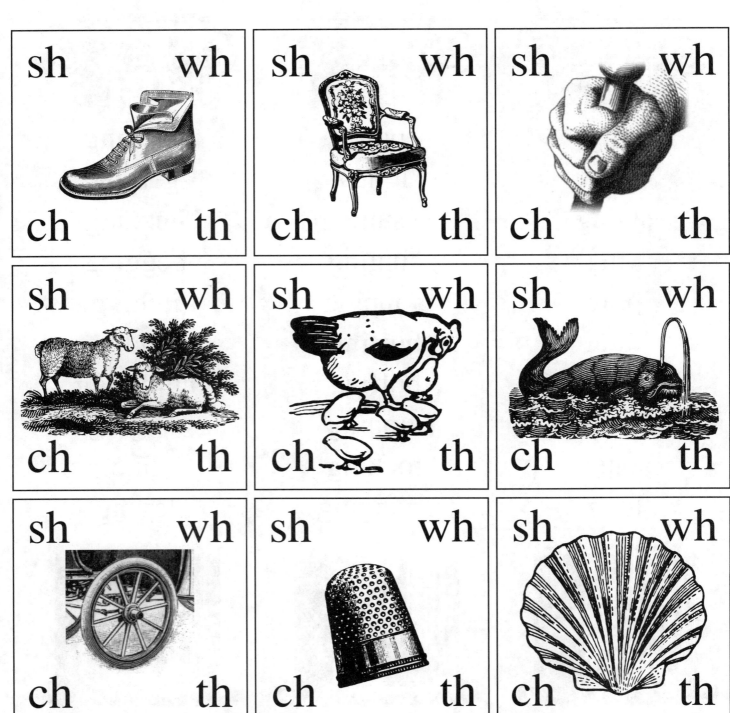

INSTRUCTIONS:
Circle the beginning sound for each picture.

sh	wh
ch	th

sh	wh
ch	th

sh	wh
ch	th

sh	wh
ch	th

sh	wh
ch	th

sh	wh
ch	th

sh	wh
ch	th

sh	wh
ch	th

sh	wh
ch	th

ing/ang /ong

INSTRUCTIONS:
Draw a line to match the word on the left to the picture on the right.

ring

king

sledding

singing

ing/ang /ong

Name

Worksheet 9B
Writing

INSTRUCTIONS:
Follow the mazes below then write out the following ING words beside the corresponding mazes.

singing

hopping

running

begging

dipping

ELLA SINGS JAZZ

INSTRUCTIONS:
Circle the correct answer.

1. When Ella was set to sing, she sang with _____.
JOHN   CHICK   JEFF

2. What songs did Ella sing? (circle two)
JAZZ   POP   FOLK

3. Ella's fans said Ella had _____ lungs for singing.
BAD   FAT   TOP

ing/ang /ong

INSTRUCTIONS:
Cut "Matisse" shapes like the ones below into potato halves. Place the potato stamps into the paint and stamp the shapes onto the paper. Blocks or strips of colored construction paper can be added to complete the effect.

SUPPLIES:
Paper
Potatoes
Tempra paint (primary colors)

33

CONSONANT BLENDS

Name

INSTRUCTIONS:
Color the boxes orange that have pictures that begin with an R blend (BR, CR, DR, FR, GR, PR, TR, WR).

35

CONSONANT BLENDS

Name   *Seeing*

In some words, the letter R comes after another letter, like in *frog*. To say these words you blend the sound of the first letter with the sound of R.

INSTRUCTIONS:
Circle the blend at the beginning of each word.

frog   crop   drum

brag   crush   grab

bred   drab   grin

brig   dress   grub

crib   drip   trot

CONSONANT BLENDS

Name

INSTRUCTIONS:
Circle the R blend at the beginning of each word.

f(r)og   brick   shell

cat   thin   rat

crab   wing   ring

song   drum   grass

thing   truck   goat

CONSONANT BLENDS

Name

INSTRUCTIONS:
Copy the R blend words.

crib

frog

drum

grim

CONSONANT BLENDS

Name

INSTRUCTIONS:
Say the blend on the left with the sound on the right.

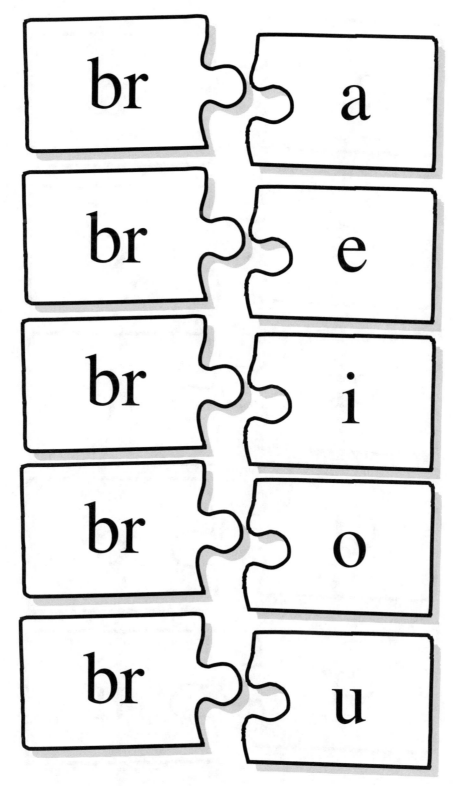

br	a
br	e
br	i
br	o
br	u

CONSONANT BLENDS

INSTRUCTIONS:
Say the blend on the left with the sound on the right.

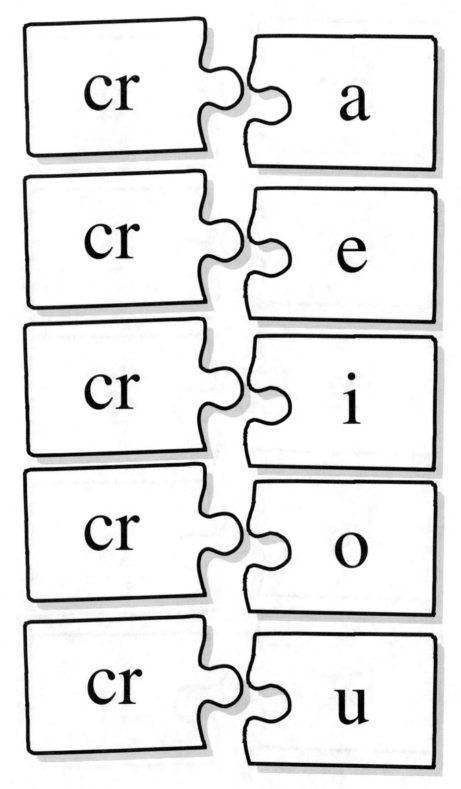

CONSONANT BLENDS

Name

INSTRUCTIONS:
Say the blend on the left with the sound on the right.

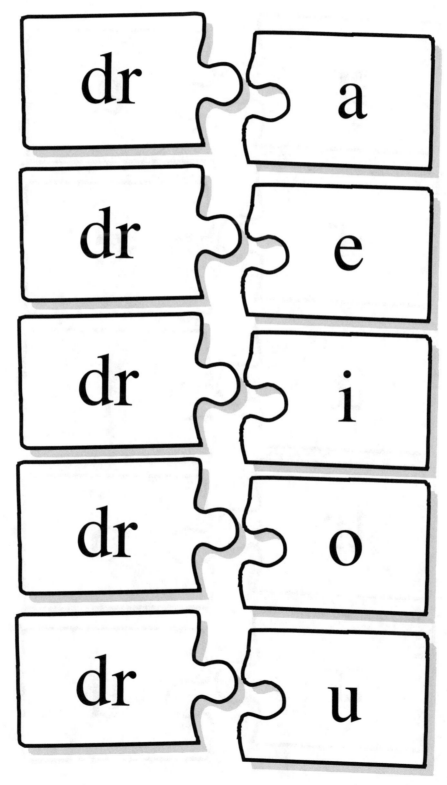

CONSONANT BLENDS

INSTRUCTIONS:
Say the blend on the left with the sound on the right.

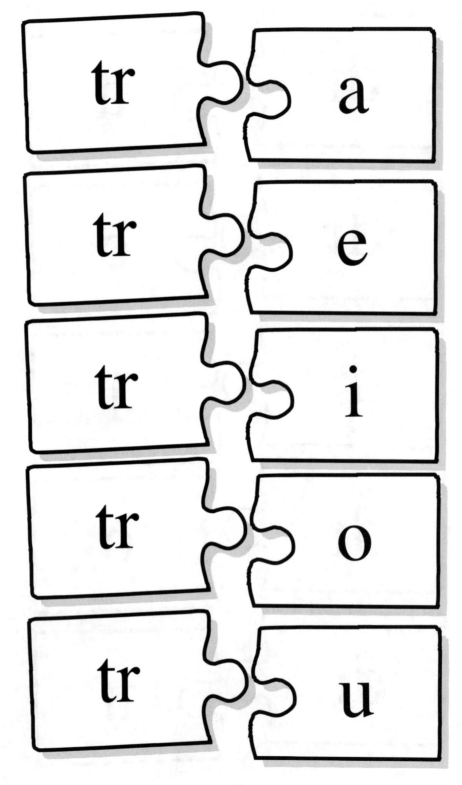

CONSONANT BLENDS

Name

INSTRUCTIONS:
Fill in the letter maze at the beginning of each row. Then circle each picture that begins with the R blend sound.

Consonant Blends

Name

INSTRUCTIONS:
When we put pieces to a puzzle together they make pictures. When we put sounds together they make words. Remember when we have an R with another letter their sounds blend together.

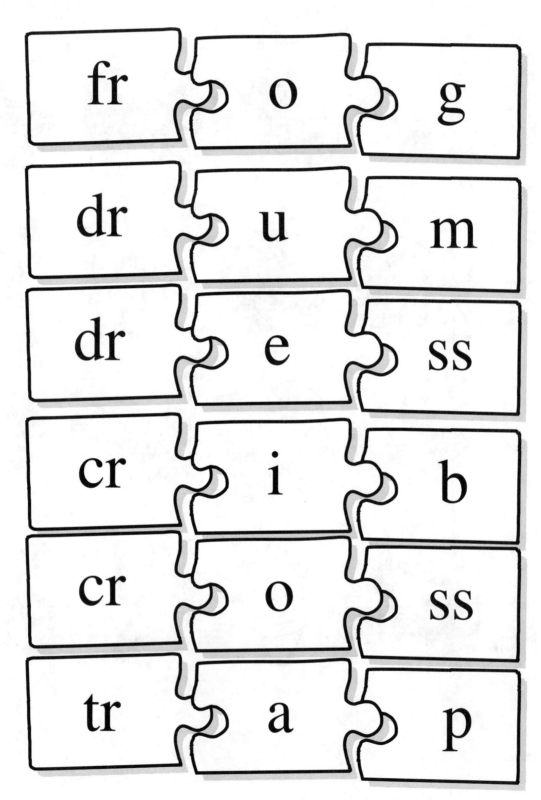

fr o g

dr u m

dr e ss

cr i b

cr o ss

tr a p

CONSONANT BLENDS

INSTRUCTIONS:
Read up and down the word columns which feature words from a book you will soon be reading about Alfred the King.

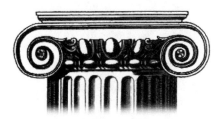

brash	brag	
trek	fret	North
press	brick	push
intrepid	prongs	send
grab	prod	who
crush	afresh	into
trap	abet	

CONSONANT BLENDS

INSTRUCTIONS:
Color the presents that have pictures that begin with an R blend (BR, CR, DR, FR, GR, PR, TR, WR)

CONSONANT BLENDS

INSTRUCTIONS:
Match the R blend words on the left with the pictures on the right.

frog

crib

dress

brick

crab

Consonant Blends

Name

INSTRUCTIONS:
In some words the letter L comes after another letter like in *black*. To say these words you blend the sound of the first letter with the sound of L. Circle the L blend at the beginning of each word and read aloud.

block   bless   slam

black   clip   slip

flag   clap   flip

glad   clock   flat

plan   cling   glut

bliss   clang   glass

CONSONANT BLENDS

INSTRUCTIONS:
Follow the mazes for the L blends, then make them on
your own.

bl

bl

clang

clock

black

CONSONANT BLENDS

Name

INSTRUCTIONS:
Color the boxes green that have pictures that begin with an
L blend (GL, PL, CL, SL)

CONSONANT BLENDS

Name

INSTRUCTIONS:
Say the blend on the left with the sound on the right.

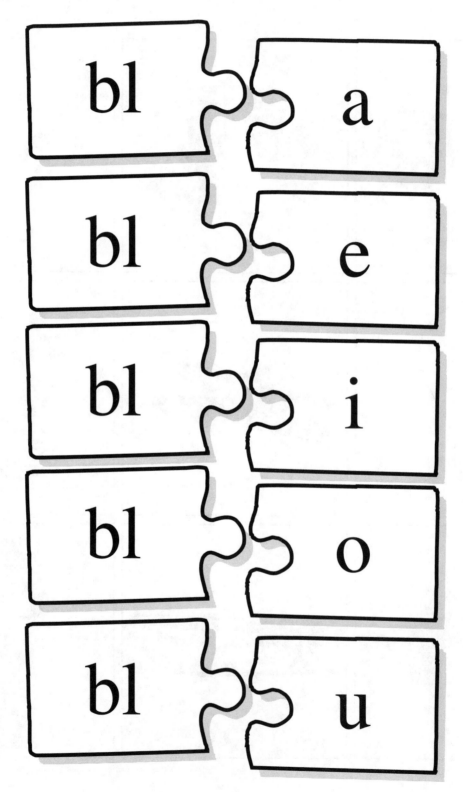

CONSONANT BLENDS

Name

INSTRUCTIONS:
Say the blend on the left with the sound on the right.

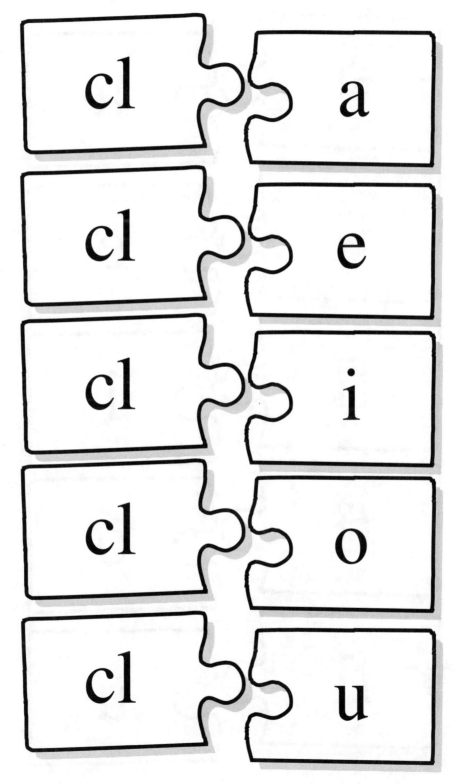

CONSONANT BLENDS

Name

INSTRUCTIONS:
Say the blend on the left with the sound on the right.

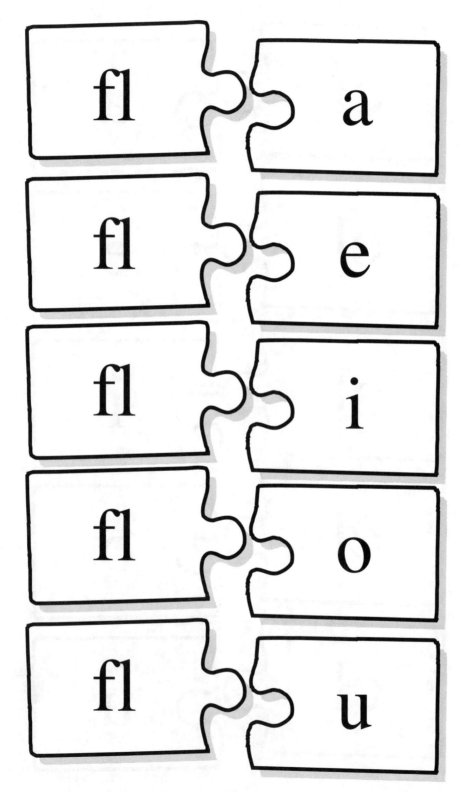

fl — a

fl — e

fl — i

fl — o

fl — u

CONSONANT BLENDS

Name

INSTRUCTIONS:
Say the blend on the left with the sound on the right.

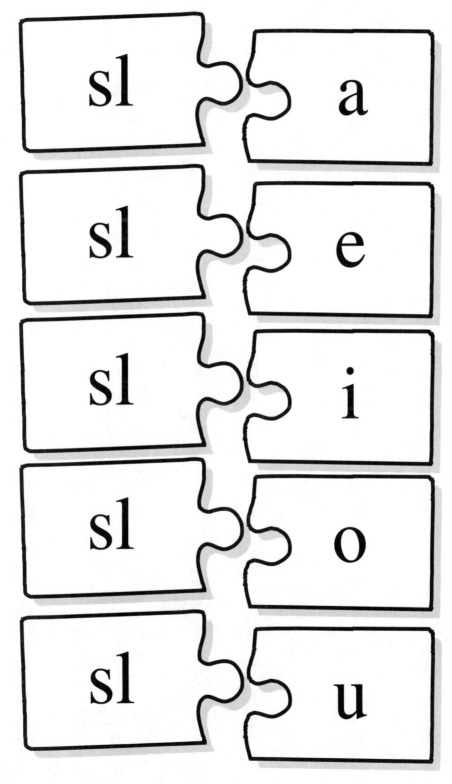

CONSONANT BLENDS

Name

INSTRUCTIONS:
Fill in the letter maze at the beginning of each row. Then circle each picture that begins with the L blend sound.

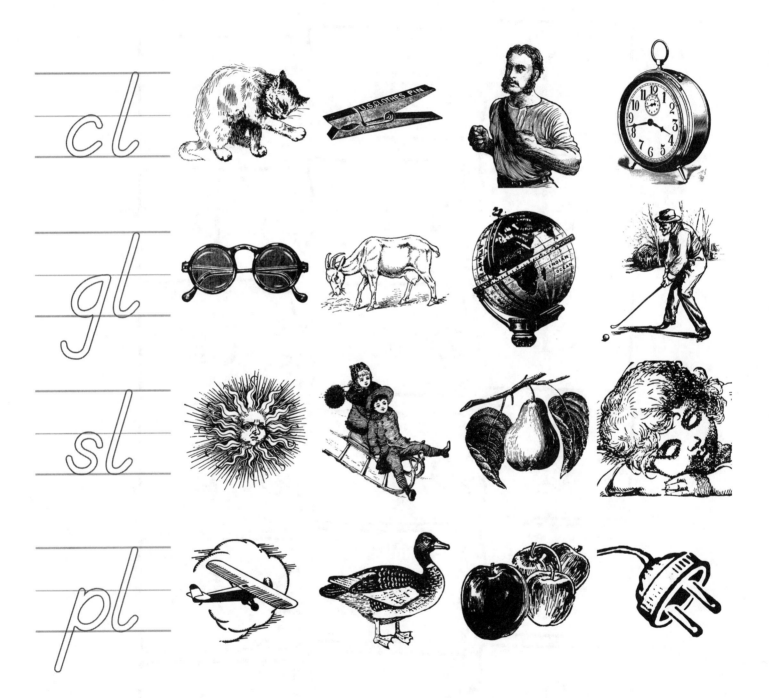

CONSONANT BLENDS

INSTRUCTIONS:
Read the words below by piecing the individual sounds together.

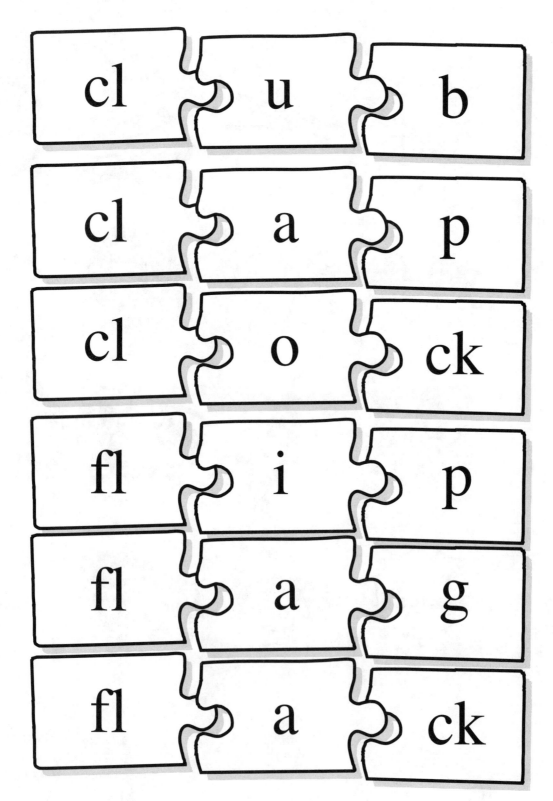

cl u b

cl a p

cl o ck

fl i p

fl a g

fl a ck

58

CONSONANT BLENDS

Name

INSTRUCTIONS:
Read up and down the word columns which feature words
from the book about Alfred the King.

Alfred	blissful	black
blot	slick	glen
cling	class	flock
plan	plot	click
flag	clang	clack
gladness	flash	slash

Name

INSTRUCTIONS:
Circle the blend for each picture.

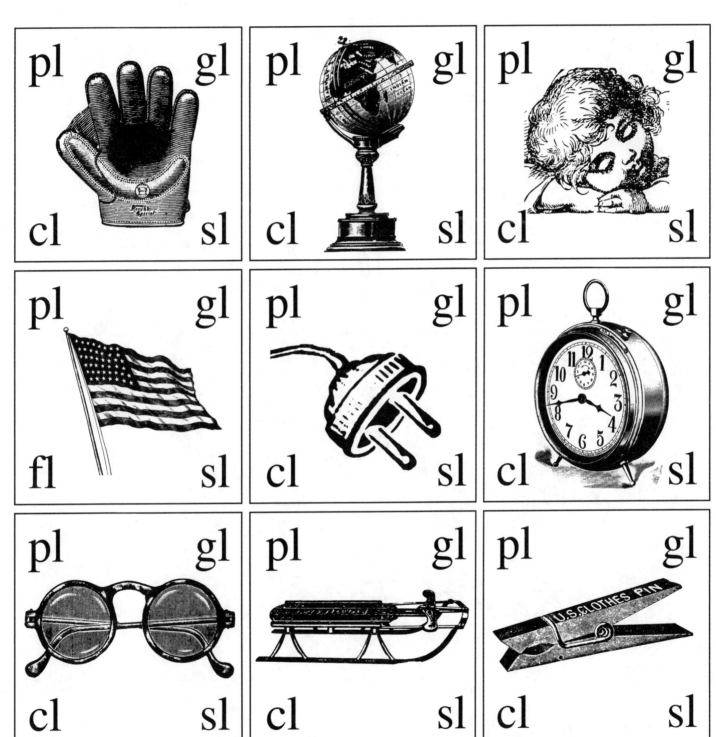

CONSONANT BLENDS

Name

INSTRUCTIONS:
Copy the L blend words.

black

block

clang

flat

sled

slam

REVIEW

INSTRUCTIONS:
Mount the circle below on cardstock then place a brass
fastner through the circle on the next page and this circle
to create a color blending wheel.

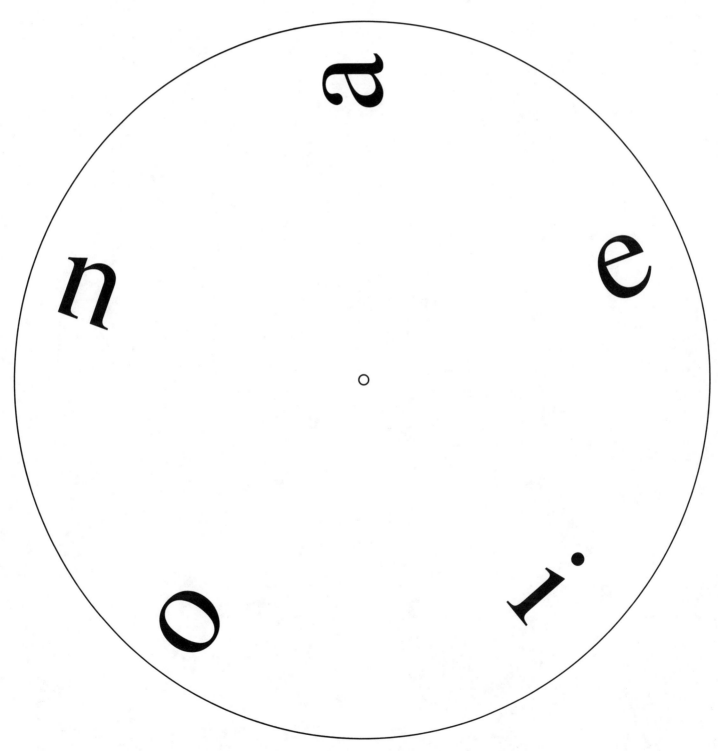

REVIEW

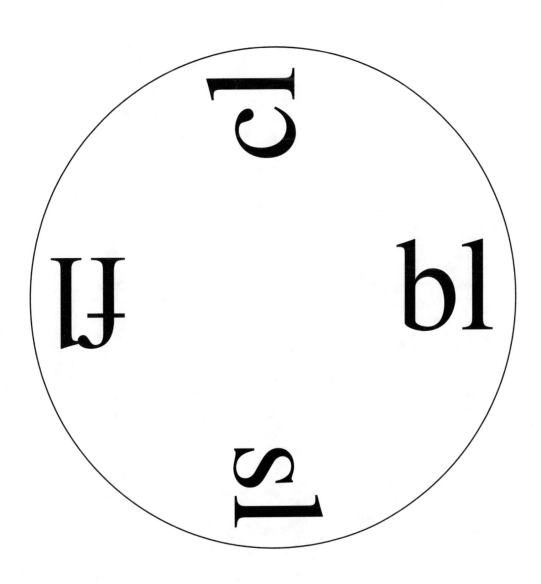

CONSONANT BLENDS

INSTRUCTIONS:
Match the blend words on the left with the pictures
on the right.

clock

dress

crab

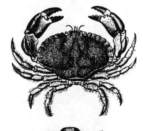

sled

flag

CONSONANT BLENDS

Name

INSTRUCTIONS:
After reading the book *Alfred the King,* connect the two ends of the strips below to make a crown. The design is based on a sculpture honoring Alfred's birthplace in Wantage, England.

ALFRED
THE KING

INSTRUCTIONS:
Match the sentence on the left to the correct picture on the right.

The brash North men did attack.

Egbert was king of the Saxons.

King Alfred and his men set up ships.

Alfred was King of Wessex.

REVIEW

Name

INSTRUCTIONS:
Fill in the beginning sound for each word.

72

TEST

INSTRUCTIONS:
Circle the blend.

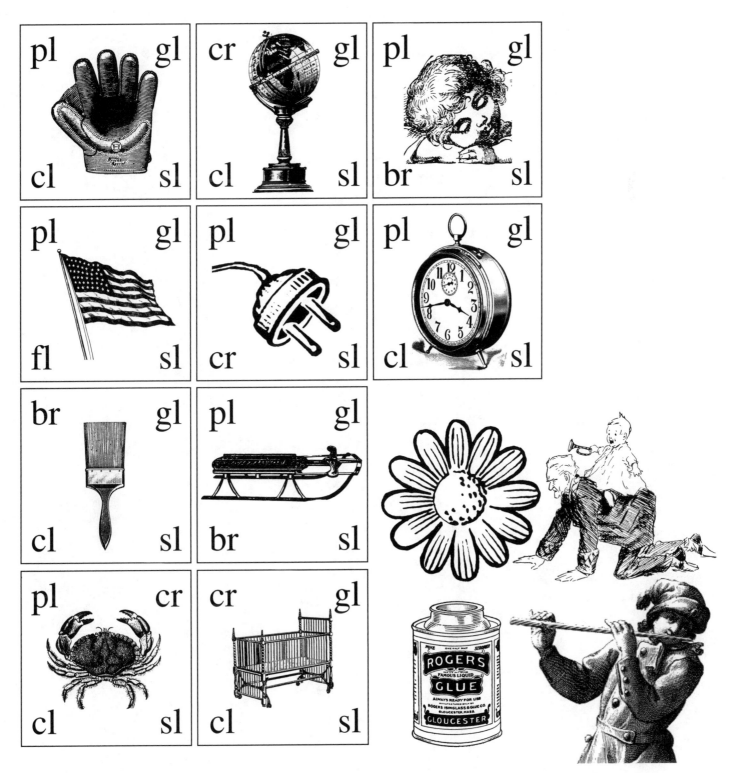

CONSONANT BLENDS

INSTRUCTIONS:
In some words the S comes before another letter like in the word *stop*. To say these words you blend the sound of S with the sound of the letter that comes after it. Circle the blend at the beginning of each word.

(stop   skip   spin

stuff   scat   swim

stick   scan   swam

skin   smell   swing

snug

CONSONANT BLENDS

INSTRUCTIONS:
Complete the mazes for these S family blends.

sc   sk   sm   sn

sp   st   sw   scr

st   sw   scr   squ

str   spr   spl

shr

CONSONANT BLENDS

INSTRUCTIONS:
Fill in the letter maze at the beginning of each row. Then circle each picture that begins with the S blend sound.

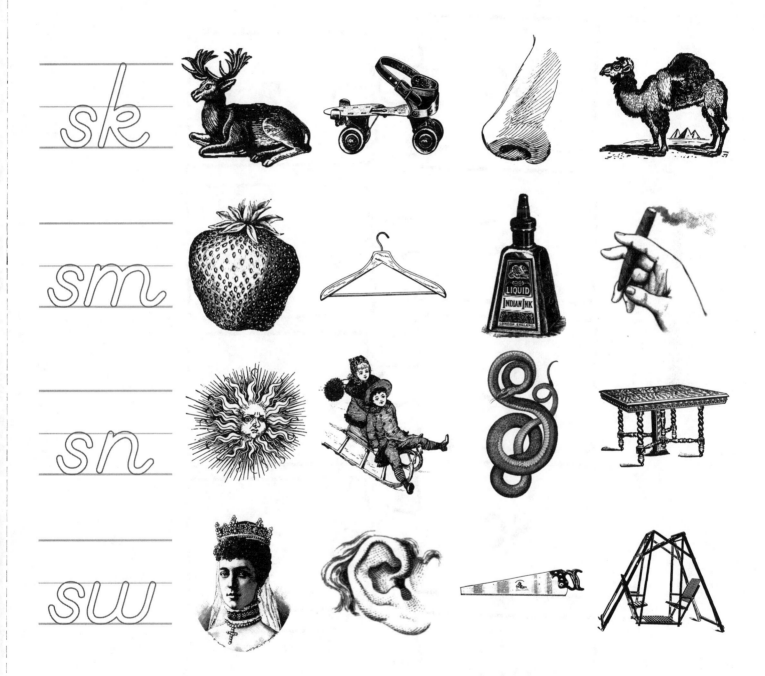

CONSONANT BLENDS

INSTRUCTIONS:
Say the blend on the left with the sound on the right.

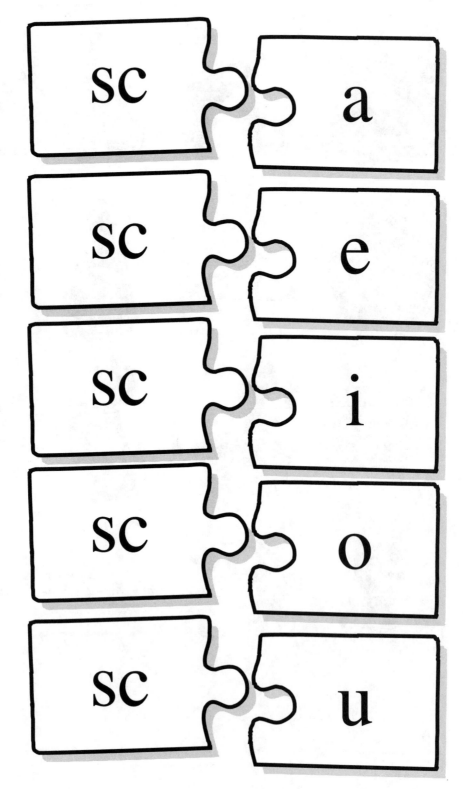

CONSONANT BLENDS

INSTRUCTIONS:
Say the blend on the left with the sound on the right.

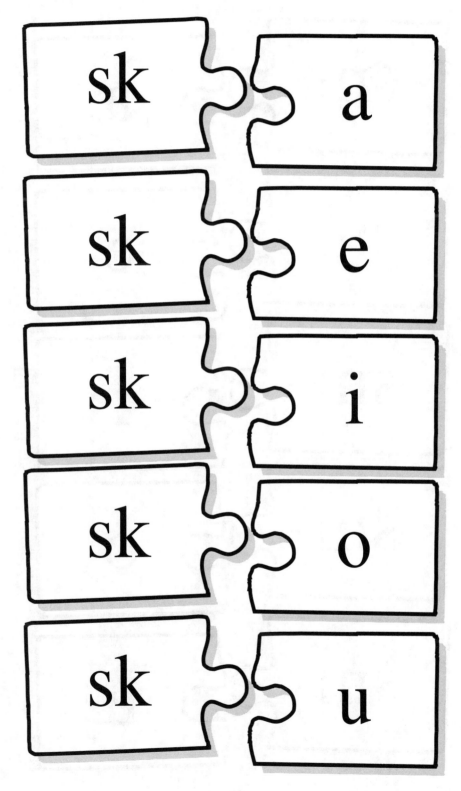

CONSONANT BLENDS

INSTRUCTIONS:
Say the blend on the left with the sound on the right.

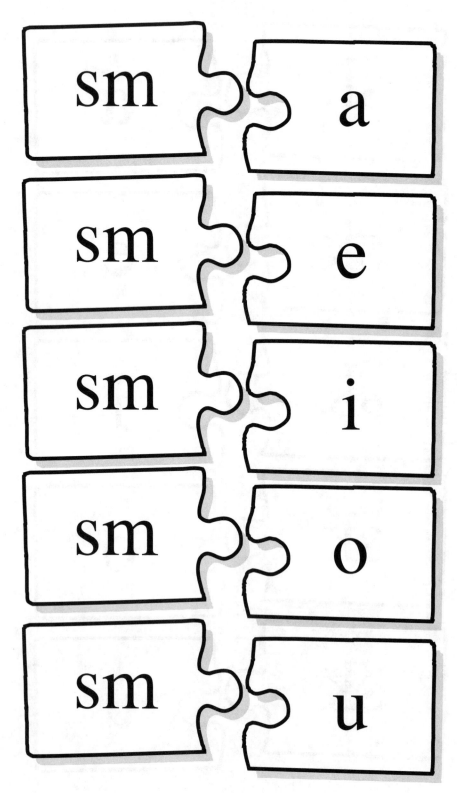

sm   a

sm   e

sm   i

sm   o

sm   u

CONSONANT BLENDS

Name

INSTRUCTIONS:
Say the blend on the left with the sound on the right.

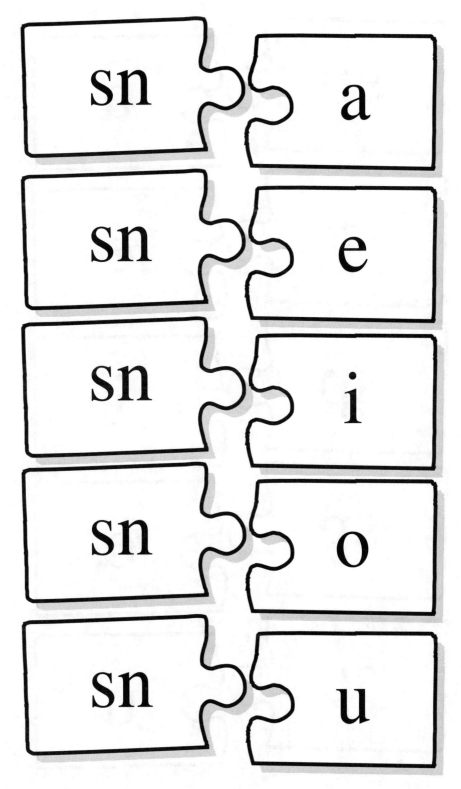

sn	a
sn	e
sn	i
sn	o
sn	u

CONSONANT BLENDS

Name

INSTRUCTIONS:
Say the blend on the left with the sound on the right.

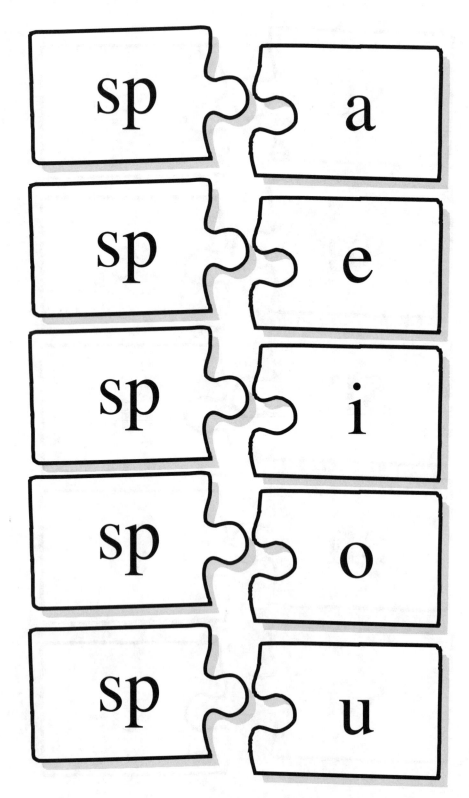

CONSONANT BLENDS

I NSTRUCTIONS:
Say the blend on the left with the sound on the right.

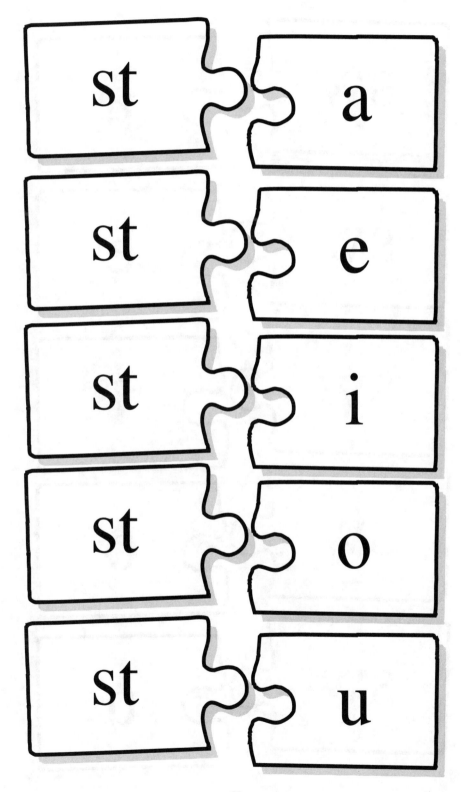

st   a

st   e

st   i

st   o

st   u

CONSONANT BLENDS

Name

INSTRUCTIONS:
Say the blend on the left with the sound on the right.

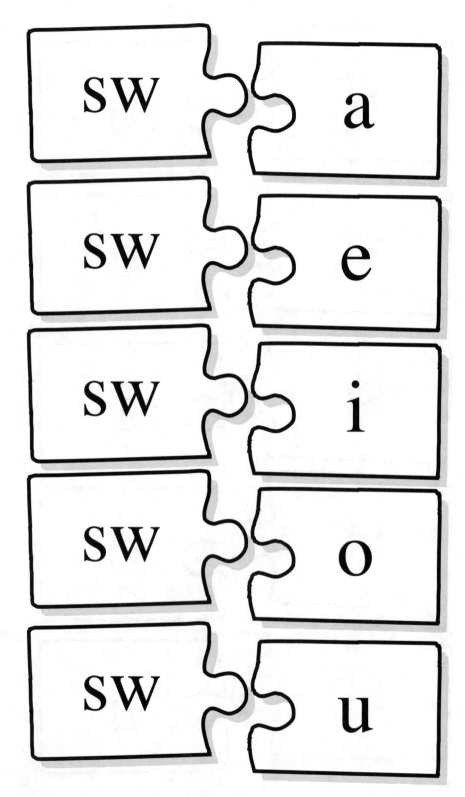

CONSONANT BLENDS

Name

INSTRUCTIONS:
Read the words below by piecing the individual sounds together.

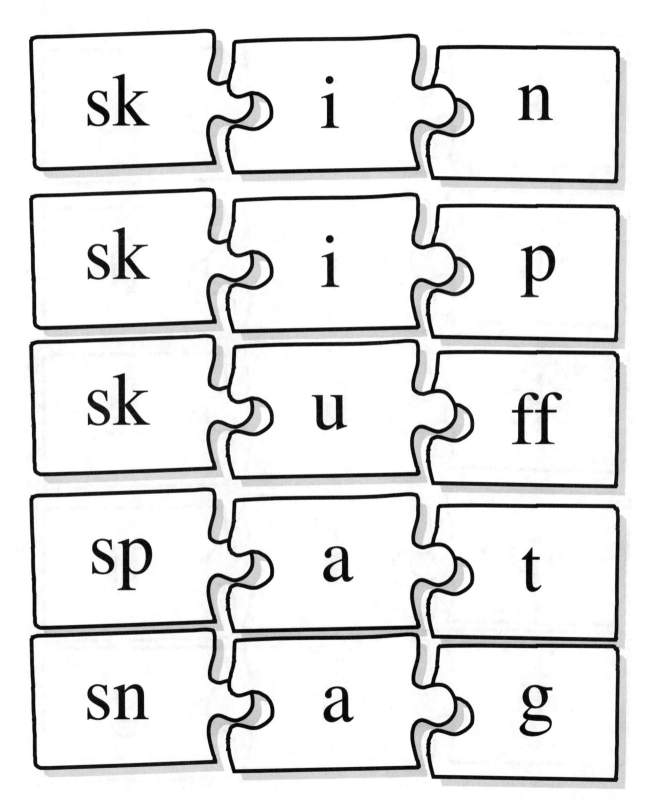

sk	i	n
sk	i	p
sk	u	ff
sp	a	t
sn	a	g

CONSONANT BLENDS

INSTRUCTIONS:
Read the words below by piecing the individual sounds together.

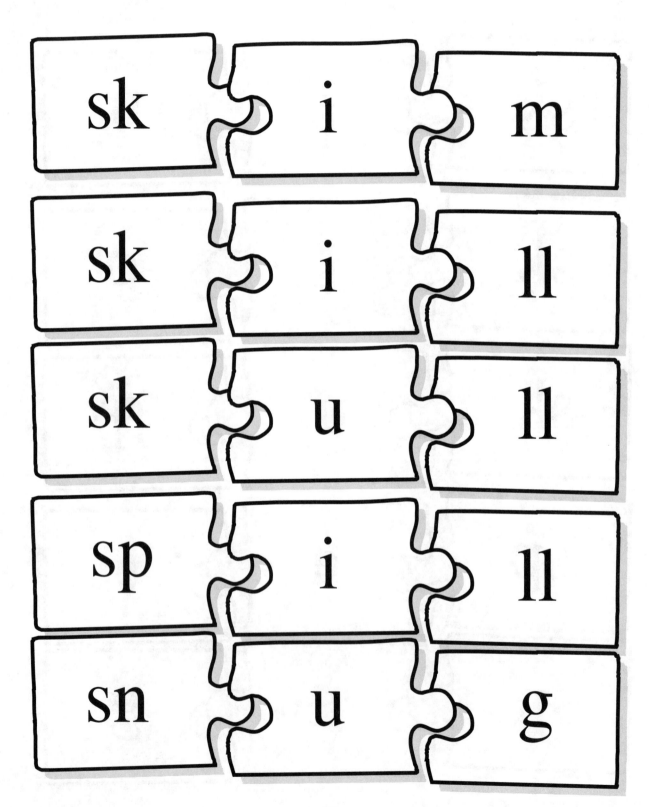

sk	i	m
sk	i	ll
sk	u	ll
sp	i	ll
sn	u	g

Consonant Blends

INSTRUCTIONS:
Copy the S blend words.

snug

scan

smell

stop

scat

swim

CONSONANT BLENDS

Name

INSTRUCTIONS:
Circle the correct letter for each picture's beginning sound.

sl sc sm   sl sk sm   sl st sm   sn sk sm

sl sk sm   sl sw sm   sl sk sm   sl sk st

CONSONANT BLENDS

Name

Reading

INSTRUCTIONS:
Read up and down the word columns.

scan	smash	step
scrip	spring	stock
scroll	stab	stop
scuff	stack	strap
skid	staff	string
skill	stag	strong
skip	stash	swim
small	stem	swing

CONSONANT BLENDS

Name

INSTRUCTIONS:
Some beginning consonant blends have three letters (SCR, SQU, STR, SPR, SPL, SHR, SCH). Read the words below by piecing the individual sounds together.

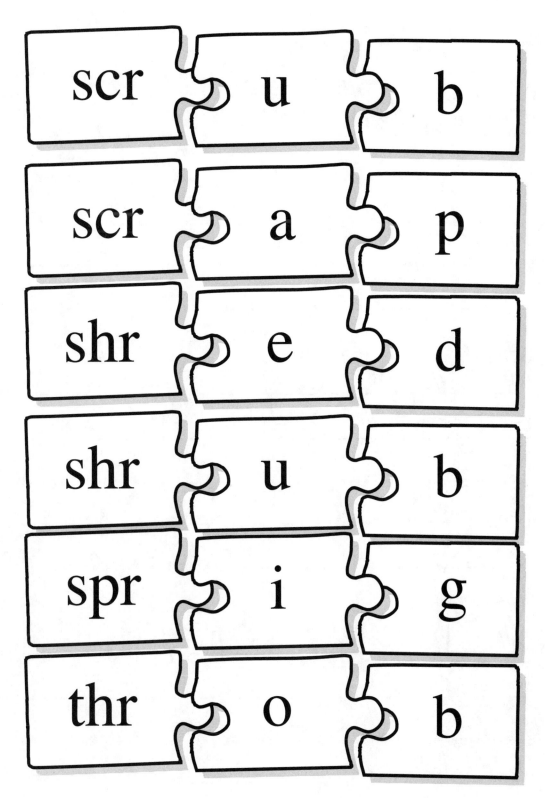

scr	u	b
scr	a	p
shr	e	d
shr	u	b
spr	i	g
thr	o	b

CONSONANT BLENDS

INSTRUCTIONS:
Complete the mazes below then copy the S blend words.

squall

scrap

spring

throb

strong

shrub

REVIEW

_____
Name

INSTRUCTIONS:
Fill in the letter maze at the beginning of each row. Then circle each picture that begins with the corresponding beginning consonant blend.

Name

REVIEW

INSTRUCTIONS:
Fill in the letter maze at the beginning of each row. Then circle each picture that begins with the corresponding beginning consonant blend.

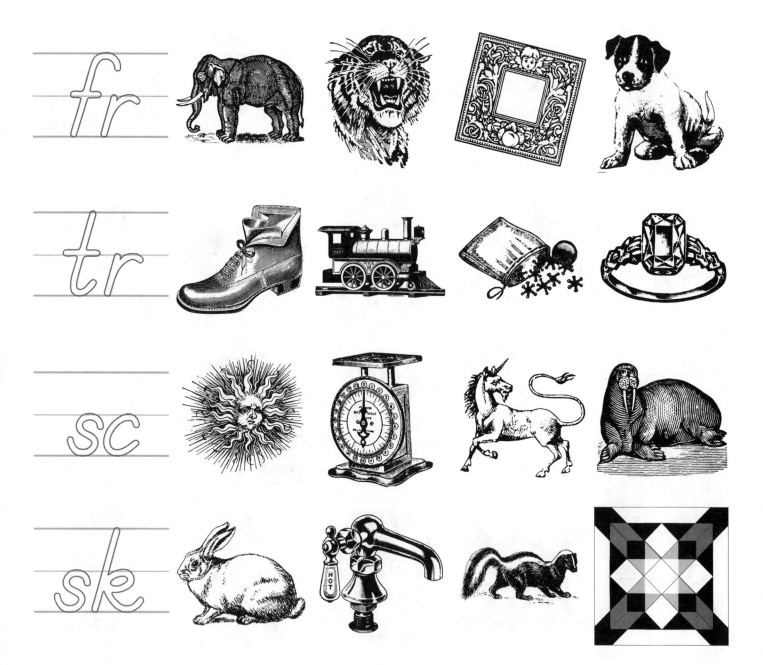

REVIEW

INSTRUCTIONS:
Match the blend words on the left with the pictures on the right.

brush

bricks

crib

drums

skull

Name

CONSONANT BLENDS

INSTRUCTIONS:
Read the words below by piecing the individual sounds together.

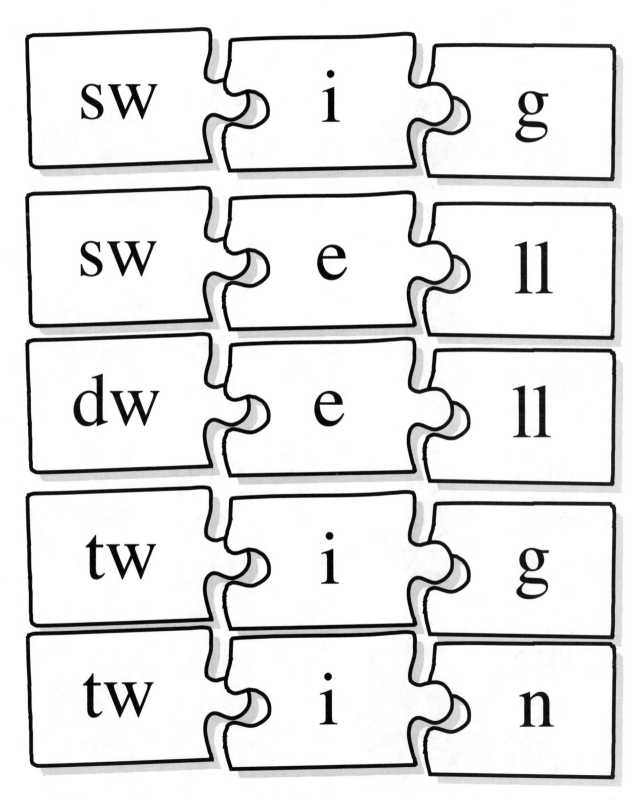

sw | i | g

sw | e | ll

dw | e | ll

tw | i | g

tw | i | n

Name

REVIEW

INSTRUCTIONS:
Circle the correct word for each picture.

snag
frog
smog

frog
drum
trap

drip
dress
grass

crab
flag
slip

block
clock
flock

sled
slick
slat

grim
crab
crib

plug
drug
shrug

REVIEW

INSTRUCTIONS:
Read up and down the columns of special exhibit words.

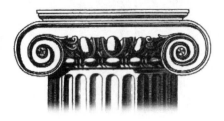  

a	you	use
and	from	eye
is	have	give
of	for	love
the	he	push
to	said	send
his	your	who
I	are	bush
they	by	her
was	one	me
all	or	put
were	been	go
what	my	their
be	she	
has	there	

99

PREPOSITIONS

INSTRUCTIONS:
Flys can get in the most unusual places. Read the words on the left and match to the picture on the right.

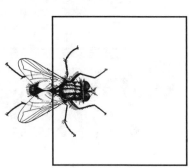

within

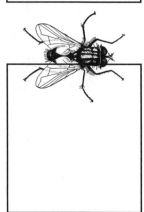

upon

onto

into

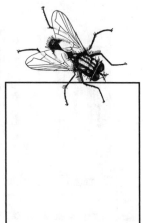

MY CLARA

INSTRUCTIONS:
Match the sentence on the left to the correct picture on the right.

The thrush did switch into a lass! She was a nix in a splendid dress.

Clara did stretch to snatch the ring from the thrush.

There were small steps which led her up within the big black walnut.

Clara did love the smell of the snapdragons and to nap on the splendid grass.

MY CLARA

INSTRUCTIONS:
Color the trunk of the tree and the bird. Then paste torn green tissue paper on the page to form the leaves of the tree.

MY CLARA

Name

INSTRUCTIONS:
Circle the correct answers to the questions below.

1. What was Clara up to in the garden?

    SLEEPING   WEEDING   SNACKING

2. What was missing in the garden?

    ANTS   SINGING   ROCKS

3. What was on the tip of the bird?

    HAT   BALL   RING

4. What did the bird call to Clara?

    "STOP!"   "CLARA, MY CLARA"   "I WANT A CRACKER"

5. The thrush did switch into a _____?

    LAD   LASS   FROG

MY CLARA

Name

INSTRUCTIONS:
Use your imagination and draw a picture below showing how you imagine the nix first was turned into a thrush.

REVIEW

INSTRUCTIONS:
After looking at each picture say its name. Write the short vowel sound in each picture.

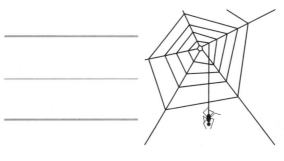

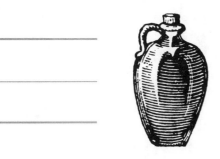

Consonant Blends

INSTRUCTIONS:
At the end of some words two letters appear together. To say these words, sound the sounds together. Circle the blend at the end of each word (ST, SK, ND, NK, NT, MP).

du(st)   mask   pump

desk   nest   crank

risk   hand   plant

fist   bank   skunk

task   band   sink

CONSONANT BLENDS

INSTRUCTIONS:
Complete the mazes below.

dust   st

damp   mp

risk   sk

hand   nd

bank   nk

mint   nt

Consonant Blends

Name

INSTRUCTIONS
Choose from the following final blends and fill in the missing letters: SK, ST

ma__ che__ ve__

ne__ fi__ de__

CONSONANT BLENDS

Name

INSTRUCTIONS:
Read the words below by piecing the individual sounds together.

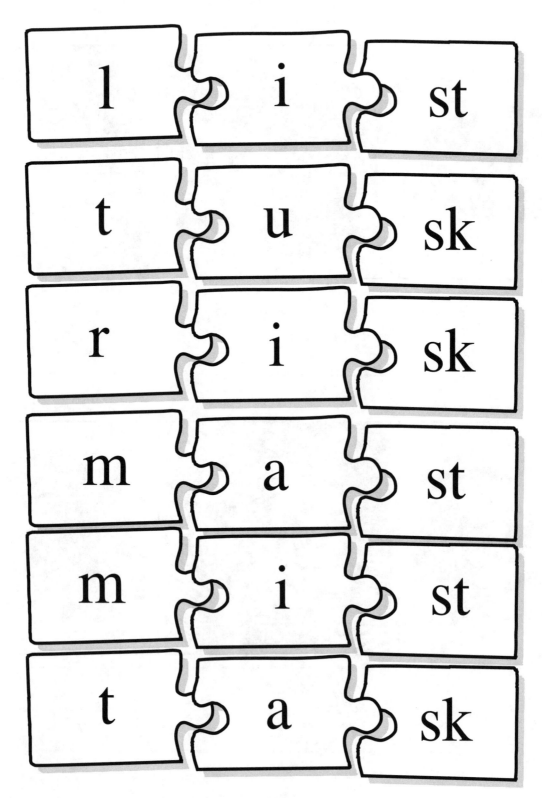

CONSONANT BLENDS

Name

INSTRUCTIONS
Choose from the following final blends (ND, NK, NT, MP) and fill in the missing letters.

sta

te

la

sku

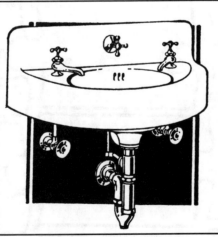

si

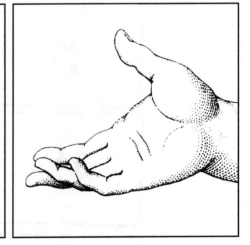

ha

113

CONSONANT BLENDS

I N S T R U C T I O N S :
Read the words below by piecing the individual sounds together.

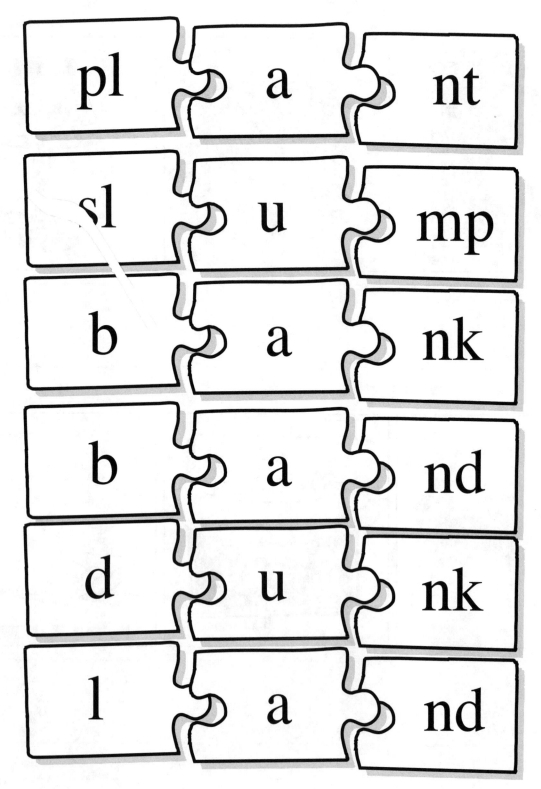

REVIEW

INSTRUCTIONS:
Read up and down the columns of words found in the next book you will read.

Holland	shelf	theft
kept	black	rend
Atlantic	felt	slink
land	last	next
along	stilt	assist
windmill	distant	diligent
pump	swift	spunk
dampness	hand	grasp
blond	crumb	luck
glint	gust	pluck
blink	sent	swept
bunk	whisk	glint
blink	swept	jump
slept	twist	gasp
prompt	plunging	bolt
stand	second	pelt
climb	crest	wilt
except	kept	limp
plant	instant	wimp
bulb	halt	grand
milk	grump	

THE GRAND CAT

INSTRUCTIONS:
Circle the correct answers to the questions below.

1. Wim was a _____ cat.

    FAT   RED   SLACK

2. Ma had left a glass of milk and a _____ for Frans.

    CAR   BUN   PIG

3. A gust of wind sent his _____ aloft.

    HAT   SHIRT   CAT

4. Katrin and Frans set to bumping at the
    windmill with a _____?

    HAT   STILT   DUCK

5. What went limp on the windmill?

    DRESS   CAT   HAT

THE GRAND CAT

Name

INSTRUCTIONS:
Cut out the pictures on the right. Glue them onto the blocks on the left, in the order they occurred in the story.

Name

THE GRAND CAT

INSTRUCTIONS:
Make a windmill.

SUPPLIES:
- *Square sheet of paper*
- *Brass fastener*
- *Milk carton*
- *Paints or markers*

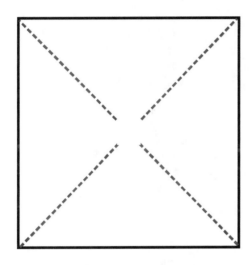
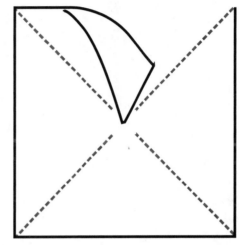

VOWEL + R

INSTRUCTIONS:
When followed by an R, A, E, I, O, and U make a special
sound. The same sound is made by ER, IR and UR. Circle
the AR, ER, IR, OR, and UR in the following words.

car   burn   fur

fern   horn   card

bird   far   shirt

term   fork   girl

corn   star   barn

VOWEL + R

INSTRUCTIONS:
Complete the mazes below.

corn   shirt

fern   horn

burn   fork   jar

term   dirt

bird   yard

letter car fur

VOWEL + R

INSTRUCTIONS:
Read the words below by piecing the individual sounds together.

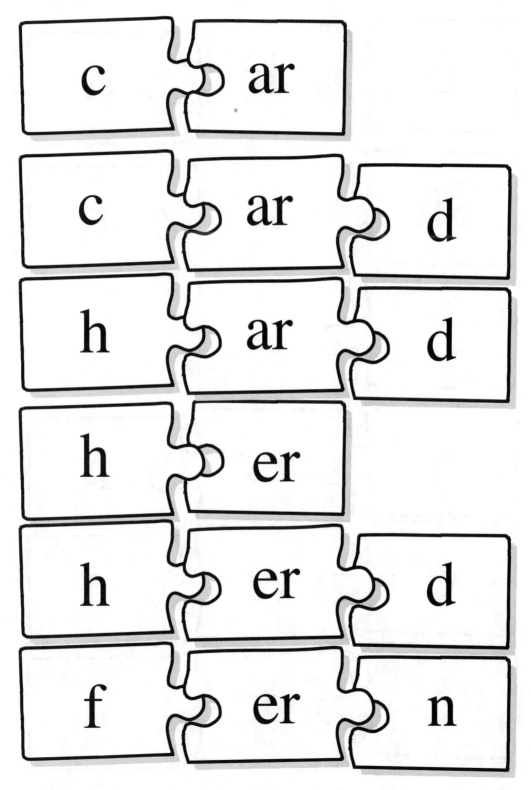

c — ar

c — ar — d

h — ar — d

h — er

h — er — d

f — er — n

125

VOWEL + R

INSTRUCTIONS:
Read the words below by piecing the individual sounds together.

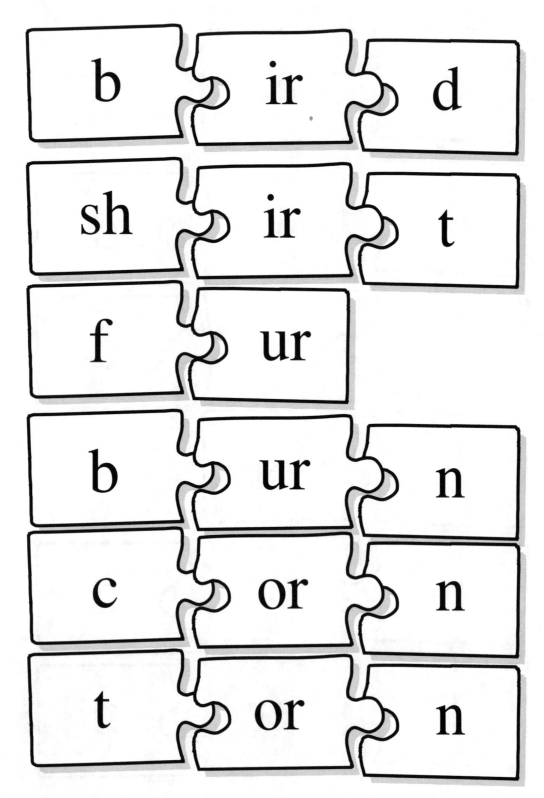

Name

VOWEL + R

INSTRUCTIONS:
Circle the correct word for each picture.

card
star
car

far
car
jar

fork
short
fort

bird
burn
farm

torn
corn
shorn

horn
storm
form

cart
card
barn

hammer
letter
ladder

Name

REVIEW

INSTRUCTIONS

Choose from the following list of words and write the correct word for each picture.

girl, farm, corn, shark, skirt, zipper, star, fork

VOWEL + R

INSTRUCTIONS:
The ER sound can also be found at the end of some words. When ER is at the end of a word the ending means "one who" or "that which." Read the following words out loud.

sit
sitter

cut
cutter

camp
camper

drum
drummer

run
runner

farm
farmer

spin
spinner

jump
jumper

big
bigger

REVIEW

Name

INSTRUCTIONS:
Trace the mazes to create the upper case letters then write the lower case letters beside the upper case letters.

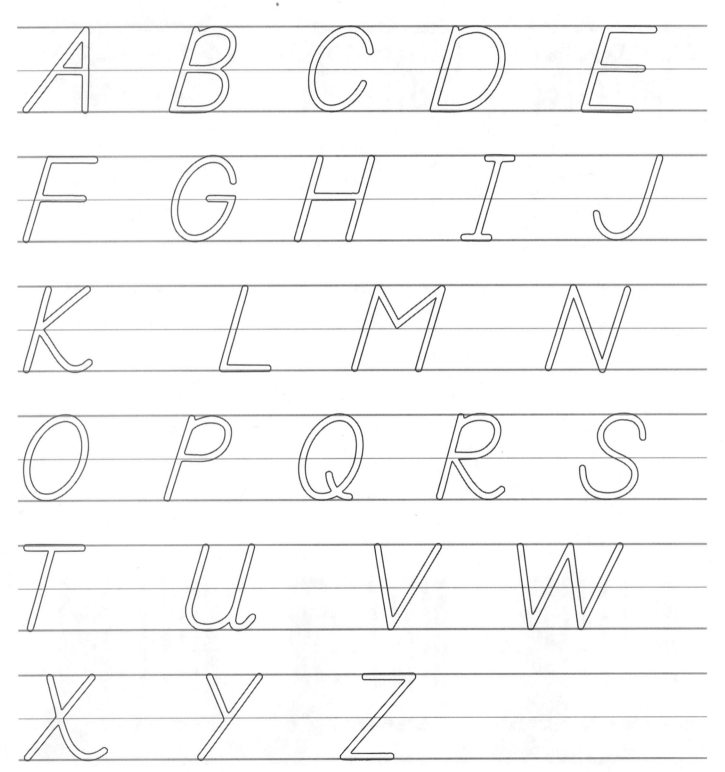

Vowel + R

Read up and down the columns of words from the book
The Black Flag.

buccaneers	smirk	stir
lurk	snarl	harbor
stern	Lord	apart
whirl	lurch	Cotton
bark	gird	Mather
tarp	start	furl
swan	herd	swirl
Word	locker	perch
port	snort	surrender
pastor	hurl	water
arms	spar	
terms	dart	

THE BLACK FLAG

Name

INSTRUCTIONS:
Match the word on the left to the correct picture on the right. There are more words than there are pictures.

cutter

swords

shark

fork

shirt

fir

robbers

locker

133

THE BLACK FLAG

Name _____

INSTRUCTIONS:
After reading *The Black Flag,* answer the following questions.

1. What was hurling in the water?

    TRUCK   CUTTER   FISH

2. What did the black flag have on it?

    SKULL   CROSS   LETTERS

3. What went whirling into the cutter's rigging?

    FISH   CANNON BALLS   BOXES

4. What was the locker full of?

    CATS   GUNS   SILVER

5. Fill in the blank. Cotton Mather was a _____?

    FLAG   ROBBER   PASTOR

TEST

INSTRUCTIONS:
Circle the beginning blend for the pictures in the first block, the correct vowel + R words in the second block and the ending blends in the third block.

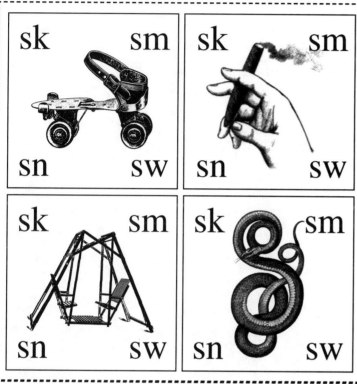

bird
burn
farm

horn
storm
form

135

LONG VOWELS

_____
Name

INSTRUCTIONS:
Circle the words that have two vowels, with the second one being an E.

hat   ride   bad

(hate)   rid   bade

kite   tub   ton

kit   tube   tone

not   dime   pipe

note   dim   pip

The letters a, e, i, o, and u are called vowels. We have learned the sounds of these letters but sometimes they may sound different. There is a rule that will help know when to make the different sound: *A, E, I, O and U usually keep their names, when a silent final E is near—as in cute and bike and game.*

CONSONANT BLENDS

Name

INSTRUCTIONS:
Color the boxes blue that have pictures that have the sound of long A (as in *plate*).

LONG VOWELS

Name

INSTRUCTIONS:
Practice making the shapes of the long vowel words below by first drawing within the letter outlines then creating the letter shapes on your own.

bake

wane

save

male

daze

crate

LONG VOWELS

INSTRUCTIONS:
Color the boxes red that have pictures that have the sound of long I.

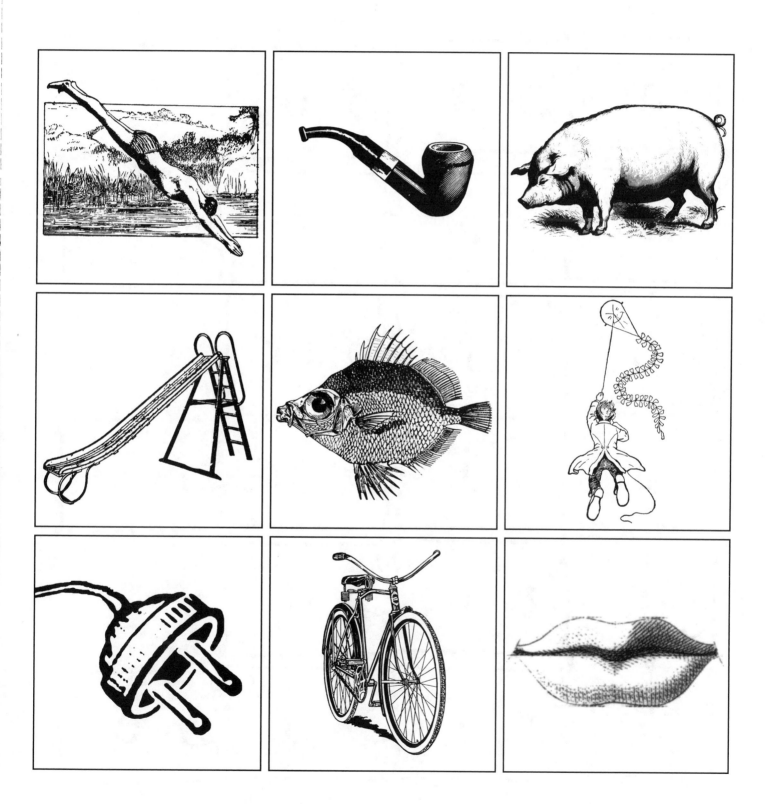

LONG VOWELS

INSTRUCTIONS:
Read the words below by piecing the individual sounds together.

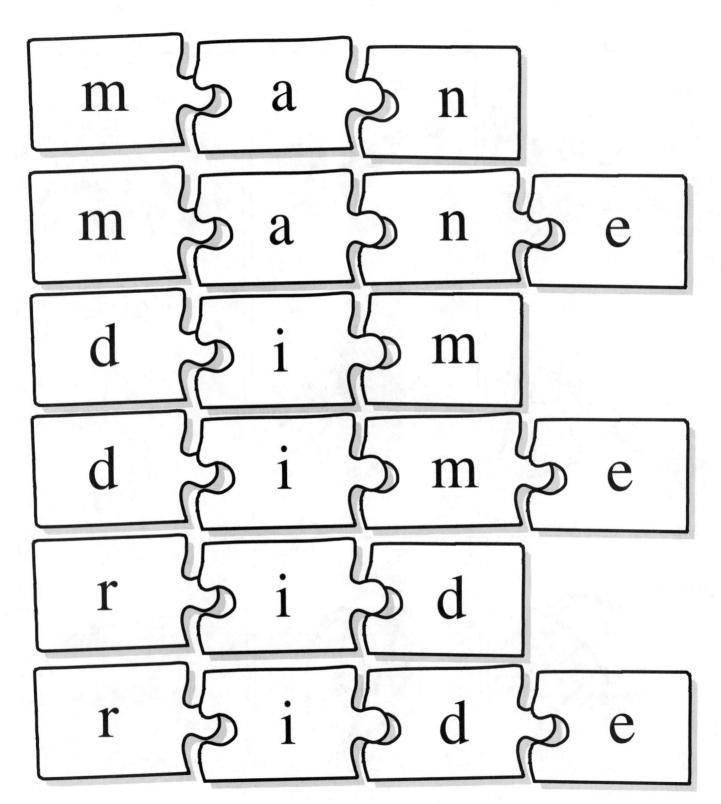

m a n

m a n e

d i m

d i m e

r i d

r i d e

142

LONG VOWELS

Name

Hearing
Writing

INSTRUCTIONS:
Fill in the letter maze at the beginning of each row.
Then circle each picture that has the sound of long O.
Finally, trace the maze at the bottom of the page then
copy the word.

nose

Name

INSTRUCTIONS:
Circle the correct word for each picture.

not
note

pan
pane

can
cane

kit
kite

tub
tube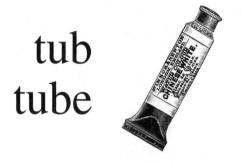

tap
tape

hat
hate

dim
dime

LONG VOWELS

_____
Name

INSTRUCTIONS:
Write out the sentence below.

The mule wore

a yoke.

LONG VOWELS

INSTRUCTIONS:
Circle the boxes red that have pictures that have the sound of long U. Then complete the maze below.

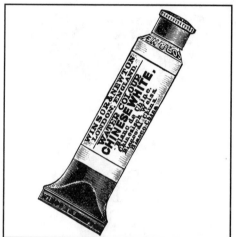

prune

LONG VOWELS

Name

INSTRUCTIONS:
Read up and down the word columns. Remember to look for two vowels and use the long vowel sound of the first vowel.

can	dim	gap
cane	dime	gape
man	rid	pet
mane	ride	Pete
hid	cut	tub
hide	cute	tube
tap	hat	pan
tape	hate	pane

148

LONG VOWELS

INSTRUCTIONS:
Say what the picture is then circle the sound of Y
you hear in each word.

long e
long i

long e
long i

long e
long i

long e
long i

long e
long i

long e
long i

The letter Y at the end of a word that contains another vowel can be heard as the long E sound as in *bunny*.
The letter Y at the end of a word that contains no other vowel or when it is in the middle of a word—like
in *myself*— can be heard as the long I sound as in *cry*.

Why, oh why, does the Y change its sound? It says E at the end of a word with a vowel.
Why, oh why, does the Y change its sound? It says I in the middle or at the end with no *vowel.*

LONG VOWELS

Name

INSTRUCTIONS:
Match the words on the left with the pictures on the right.

fly

lady

puppy

cry

bunny

pony

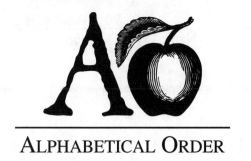

ALPHABETICAL ORDER

INSTRUCTIONS:
Place the following words in alphabetical order. Look at the first letter of each word, then place them in the order they come in the alphabet.

A B C D E F G H I J K L M N O P Q R S T U V W X Y Z

hat cat bat

1. _____

2. _____

3. _____

duck fan tag

1. _____

2. _____

3. _____

rug dog fish

1. _____

2. _____

3. _____

cake bus flute

1. _____

2. _____

3. _____

SPELLING LIST 1

INSTRUCTIONS:
Copy the words on the lines provided.

make

cake

made

ride

time

five

SPELLING LIST 1

Name

INSTRUCTIONS:
Copy the words on the lines provided.

rope

home

tune

mule

FILL IN THE BLANK:

A, E, I, O and U usually keep their names, when a silent final ____ is near—as in cute and bike and game.

153

LONG VOWELS

INSTRUCTIONS:
When we put the pieces of a puzzle together it makes a
picture. When we put letters together they make words.

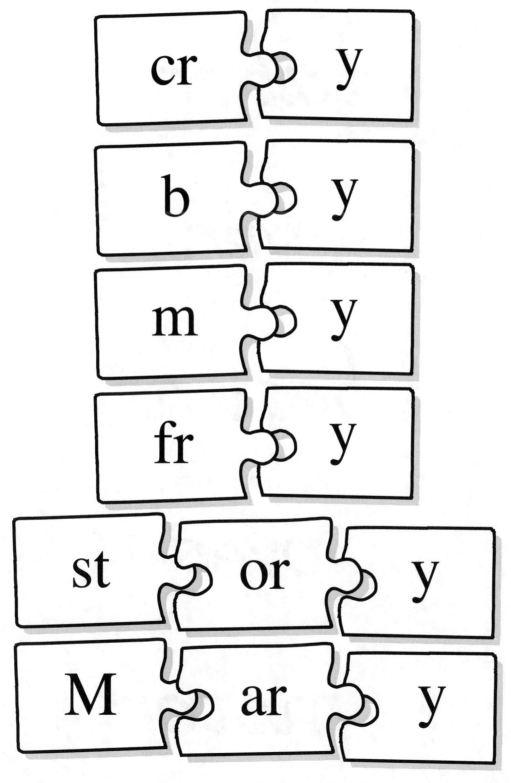

LONG VOWELS

INSTRUCTIONS:
Place a slash between the syllables in the following words.

labor

even

began

over

motor

UP IN THE SKY

INSTRUCTIONS:
Match the word on the left to the correct picture
on the right.

sky

fly

wings

bike

plane

propellers

Orville

UP IN THE SKY

INSTRUCTIONS:
After reading *Up in the Sky*, circle the correct answers to the questions below.

1. What did God give birds so that they will fly?

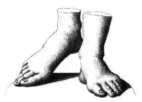  

2. What did Wilbur and Orville want?

3. What did Wilbur and Orville make?

4. Who helped Orville and Wilbur to fly?

_____

_____

_____

LONG VOWELS

Name

INSTRUCTIONS:
Copy the words on the lines provided

sky

fly

cry

penny

puppy

baby

LONG VOWELS

time	more	anger
alive	blame	angry
some	rage	debate
Bible	relate	silent
life	state	abide
dare	riding	Jesus
brave	revere	inquire
page	is	relate
share	was	here
pore	as	assembly
over	alone	close
bade	holy	never-ending

THE BRAVE MONK

1. Martin Luther was a _____.

     MONK   GIRL   KING

2. Monks spent time with the ____ and singing to God.

     CATS   FISH   BIBLE

3. The Bible said that all men must trust in _____

alone to have life with God.

     JESUS   MAN   WORK

4. Martin was a _____ monk.

     BRAVE   SAD   FAST

5. Martin felt as if he were a _____ stuck in a snare.

     DOG   HARE   CAT

SPELLING TEST 1

Name

1.

2.

3.

4.

5.

6.

7.

8.

9.

10.

VOWEL DIGRAPHS

INSTRUCTIONS:
Circle the AI or AY in each word below then draw a line through the silent partner.

rain	rail	hay
train	sail	may
grain	lay	pay
brain	play	say
mail	pray	tray
jail	clay	may

There are other spellings for the long A sound. The letter A can have a silent partner in I or Y (AI, AY).
Long A, Long A do you have a friend? Yes sir, I and Y are with me to the end. I takes me on the train;
Y likes for me to play. Either way I stay Long A every single day!

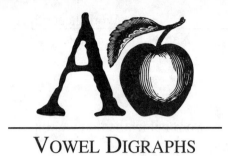

VOWEL DIGRAPHS

INSTRUCTIONS:
When we put the pieces of a puzzle together it makes a picture. When we put letters together they make words.

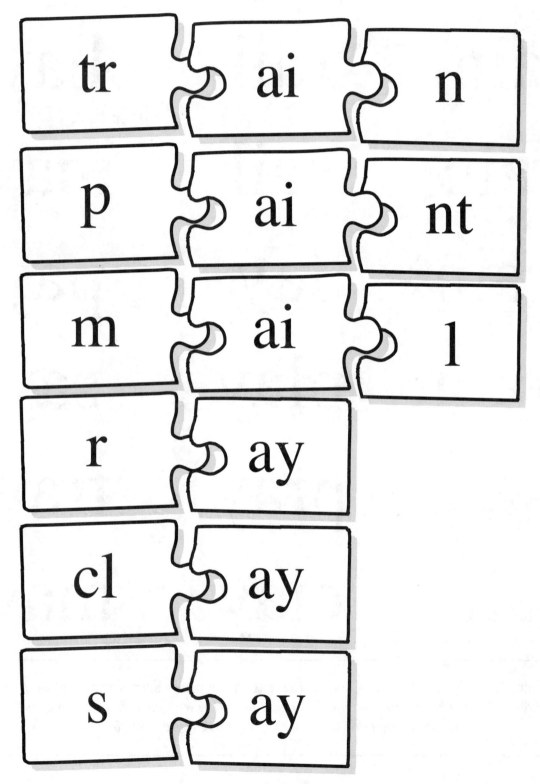

tr | ai | n

p | ai | nt

m | ai | l

r | ay

cl | ay

s | ay

Name

REVIEW

INSTRUCTIONS
Choose from the following final blends and fill in the missing letters (ST, SK, ND, NK, NT, MP).

ma＿＿＿   che＿＿＿   ve＿＿＿

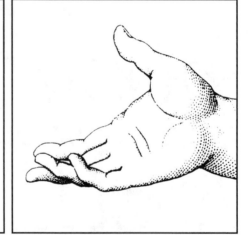

sku＿＿＿   si＿＿＿   ha＿＿＿

VOWEL DIGRAPHS

Name

INSTRUCTIONS:
Copy the words on the lines provided

rain

train

brain

play

hay

clay

VOWEL DIGRAPHS

INSTRUCTIONS:
Circle the EE or EA in each word below then draw a line through the silent partner.

tree   meet   each

deep   sheep   cream

free   green   beat

peep   bean   feast

beef   leaf   least

steep   seat   beast

Long e can also have silent partners. The first is another E as in feet. Or E can have A as a silent partner as in meat. *Long E, long E do you have a friend? Yes sir, E and A are with me to the end. E keeps me on my feet; A gives me a seat. Either way I stay Long E, which really is a treat!*

VOWEL DIGRAPHS

INSTRUCTIONS:
When we put the pieces of a puzzle together it makes a picture. When we put letters together they make words.

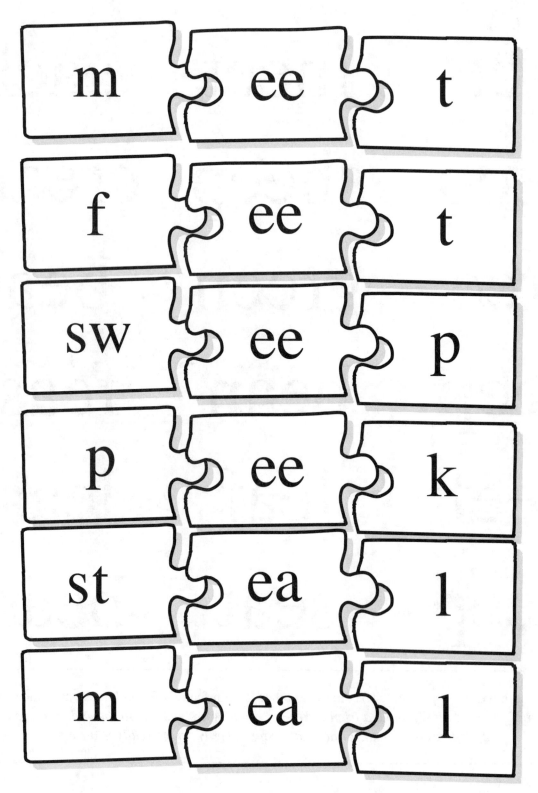

m — ee — t

f — ee — t

sw — ee — p

p — ee — k

st — ea — l

m — ea — l

VOWEL DIGRAPHS

INSTRUCTIONS:
Match the words on the left with the pictures on the right.
There are more words than pictures.

tree

read

sweep

teach

sheep

beach

leap

REVIEW

INSTRUCTIONS
Choose from the following consonant digraphs and fill in the missing letters (SH, TH, WH, CH).

_ick

_ip

_eel

_air

_ell

_ale

VOWEL DIGRAPHS

Name

INSTRUCTIONS:
Read up and down the word columns, crossing out the silent partner.

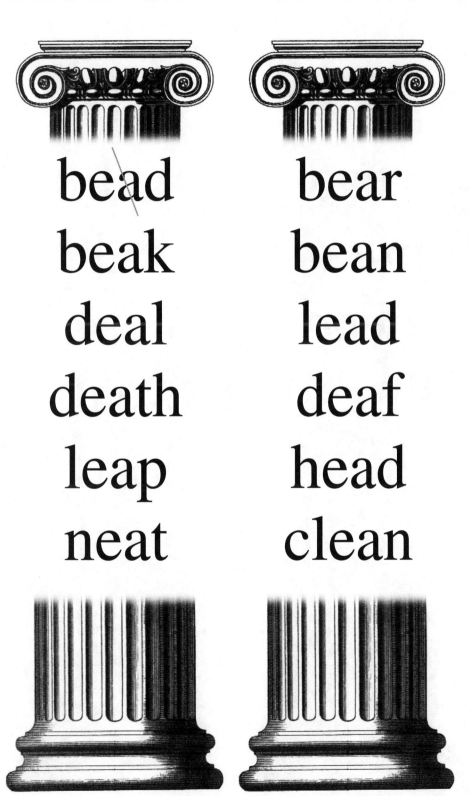

bead	bear
beak	bean
deal	lead
death	deaf
leap	head
neat	clean

Name

VOWEL DIGRAPHS

INSTRUCTIONS:
Read up and down the word columns, crossing out the silent partner.

read	health
bread	wealth
dead	steak
thread	break
dread	lead
head	bleak

VOWEL DIGRAPHS

Name

INSTRUCTIONS
Write the correct word under each picture from the
following list: LEAF, FEET, QUEEN, LEAP, TRAIN,
PRAY, EAR, BEAD, SEAL, HAY, DEER.

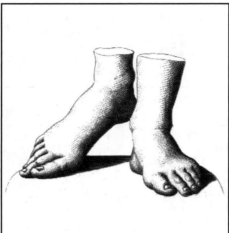

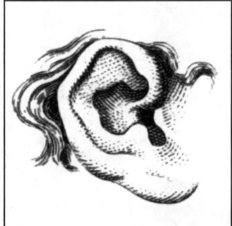

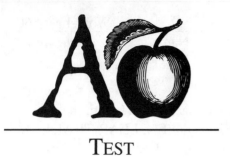

TEST

long e
long i

long e
long i

long e
long i

long e
long i

not
note

pan
pane

hat
hate

dim
dime

can
cane

kit
kite

tub
tube

tap
tape

red
read

sell
seal

card
star
car

far
car
jar

shed
sheep

tred
tree

fork
short
fort

bird
burn
farm

jar
otter
jam

chain
chip

neck
nail

car
chair

hay
hail

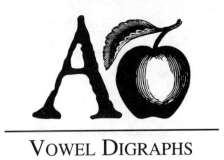

VOWEL DIGRAPHS

INSTRUCTIONS:
Circle the OA, OW, OE in each word below then draw a
line through the silent partner.

load   soap   snow

loaf   goat   hoe

road   coat   toe

toad   tow   foe

bloat   slow   woe

oak   flow

The letter O can have a silent partner, oa as in road, OE as in hoe or OW as in row.
Long O, long O do you have a friend? Yes sir, A, E, and W are with me to the end. A looks like a toad;
E tickles my toe; W helps to keeps us straight in a row!

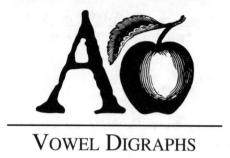

VOWEL DIGRAPHS

Name

INSTRUCTIONS:
Copy the sentence on the lines provided

The toad is on the oak.

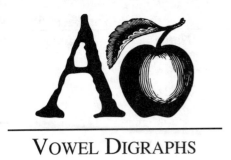

VOWEL DIGRAPHS

INSTRUCTIONS:
Read up and down the word columns.

boat	crow	toast
coat	bowl	goat
Joe	slow	loaf
woe	show	soak
yellow	low	mow
pillow	coach	grow

VOWEL DIGRAPHS

Name

INSTRUCTIONS:
Write the names of the items pictured.

boat

goat

toes

soap

bowl

hoe

VOWEL DIGRAPHS

INSTRUCTIONS:
Circle the correct word for each picture.

soap
slow

toes
row

window
yellow

boat
bowl

goes
goat

coat
boat

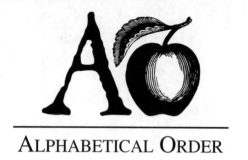

ALPHABETICAL ORDER

INSTRUCTIONS:
Place the following words in alphabetical order. Look at the first letter of each word, then place them in the order they come in the alphabet.

A B C D E F G H I J K L M N O P Q R S T U V W X Y Z

load hoe row
coat blow

road yellow boat
fellow Joe

1. _____

2. _____

3. _____

4. _____

5. _____

1. _____

2. _____

3. _____

4. _____

5. _____

180

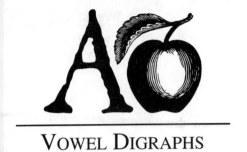

VOWEL DIGRAPHS

Name

INSTRUCTIONS:
Read each sentence then choose the word that makes the most sense and write it in the lines.

1. The _____ was red.

   coat   hoe   slow

2. The _____ was at sea.

   toast   foot   boat

3. Dad drives the car on the _____ .

   road   toad   soap

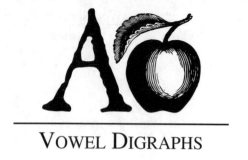

VOWEL DIGRAPHS

Name

INSTRUCTIONS:
Read each sentence then choose the word that makes the
most sense and write it in the lines.

4. The _____ was white.

yellow   snow   slow

5. The _____ was green.

toad   flow   blow

6. The _____ was in the tree.

road   float   crow

Name

REVIEW

INSTRUCTIONS:
Say the name of each picture, listening in particular
to the beginning sound. Draw a line to match the
pictures that have the same *beginning* sounds.

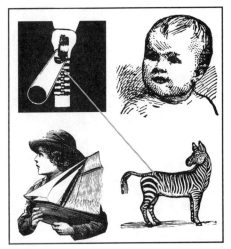

183

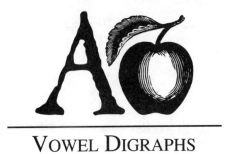

VOWEL DIGRAPHS

Name

INSTRUCTIONS:
Circle the picture in the sound row that has the same vowel digraph sound as the first picture.

soap

bowl

window

hoe

185

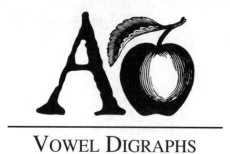

VOWEL DIGRAPHS

INSTRUCTIONS:
Match the words on the left with the pictures on the right.
There are more words than pictures.

crow

toast

tree

toes

bowl

sheet

leaf

bee

toad

window

REVIEW

INSTRUCTIONS:
Circle the beginning sound for each picture.

sh wh 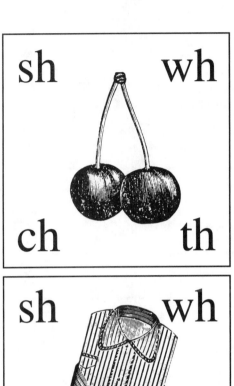 ch th	sh wh  ch th	sh wh  ch th
sh wh 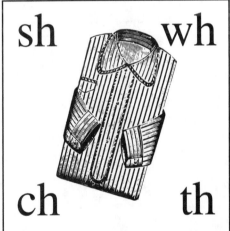 ch th	sh wh  ch th	sh wh  ch th
sh wh  ch th	sh wh 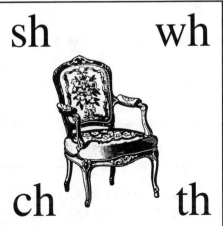 ch th	sh wh  ch th

SPELLING LIST 2

Rule: A, E and O can all have silent partners.

INSTRUCTIONS:
Write the words below.

rain

train

may

pray

see

A I and letters A Y/Put together make the sound of a LONG A/A I and A Y are in so many words/
Such as PAID, AIDE, SAY, and HAY/Food the horses eat!

SPELLING LIST 2

_____
Name

INSTRUCTIONS:
Write the words below.

tree

eat

seat

toad

foe

*E A and E E/Operate a partnership/Though one might be silent/Said together they sound just the same/
You find them sounding "E"/Like in SEED, FEED, EAT/Their GUARANTEED to always sound like "E"*

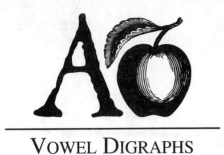

VOWEL DIGRAPHS

Name

Circle the IE in each word below then draw a line through the silent partner.

tie 　　dried　　shied

cries　　skies　　tried

fries　　die

pie　　lie

The letter I can have a silent partner in the letter E. They work together to make the sound of long I.
Long I, long I do you have friend? Yes sir, E is with me to the end. Together we can eat a pie;
In the past with D we cried. Now with S we are flying in the skies. (To the tune of Baa, Baa Black Sheep).

REVIEW

Name

INSTRUCTIONS:
Complete the alphabet dot-to-dot below.

B.   A . .Z

G.   C.

F.   .Y
H.   D.

I.   J.   E.

K.   L.   M.   .X

N.

.W

O.   .P   .U   .V

Q.   .S

.T

.R

192

VOWEL DIGRAPHS

INSTRUCTIONS:
Read up and down the word columns.

bind	sold	scroll
kind	cold	roll
find	mild	post
mind	child	most
old	toll	host
bold	troll	Christ

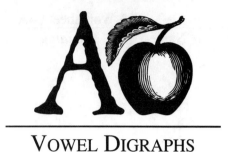

VOWEL DIGRAPHS

INSTRUCTIONS:
Copy the sentence in you best handwriting then color the picture below.

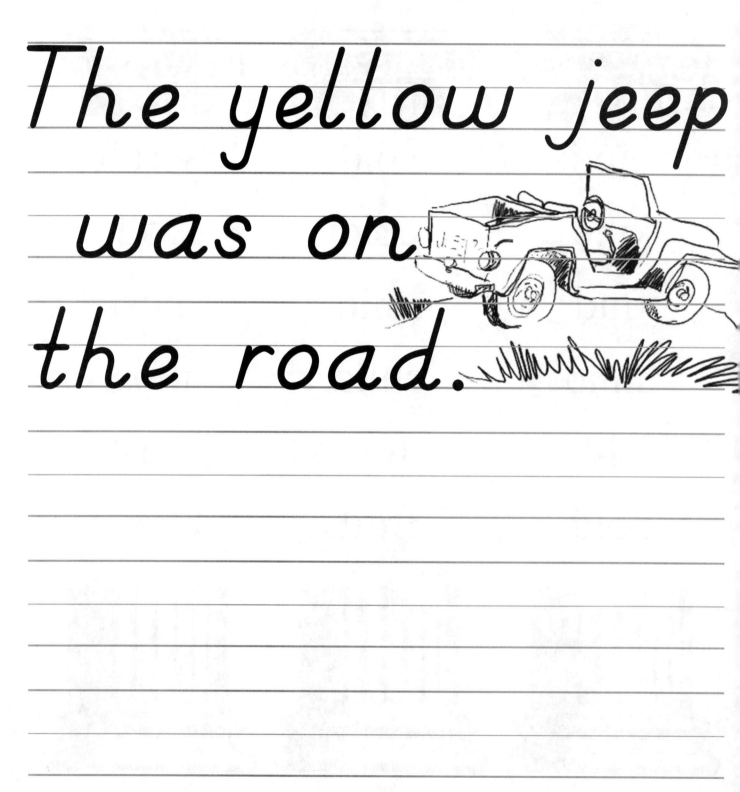

The yellow jeep was on the road.

VOWEL DIGRAPHS

INSTRUCTIONS:
Read up and down the word columns.

saint	floating	little
pray	coast	pilot
sail	wee	quay
lies	sheep	spied
may	rain	pies
day	gay	weeks
boat	way	pretty
laid	fray	cheer
oars	Easter	boar
dried	tried	bail
grain	praises	dread
sea	team	great
meals	pineapples	Christ
deep	quest	

Name *Comprehension*

THE
SAILING
SAINT

INSTRUCTIONS:
Match the words to the pictures.

monk

boat

fish

sheep

rain

whale

tan lads

bird

THE
SAILING
SAINT

Name

INSTRUCTIONS:
After reading *The Sailing Saint* circle the correct
answers to the questions below.

1. Brendan was a _____.

    MONK   DOG   DOCTOR

2. Saint Brendan told all he met of _____.

    BIRDS   FISHING   CHRIST

3. Brendan wants to go to a blest _____ that lays

  past the sunset.

    CHURCH   LAND   CLUB

4. Brendan and some monks put tan _____ over thin

  branches to make the boat..

    SHEETS   SKINS   SHIRTS

5. Brendan saw a land full of _____ and birds.

    SHEEP   DOGS   CATS

6. Brendan set on a land that rose and dove.

  The land was a _____.

    WHALE   BIRD   HORSE

7. Brendan told the lads and lasses of _____.

    PIGS   CHRIST   SAILING

THE
SAILING
SAINT

INSTRUCTIONS:
Color the picture below.

A = Brown   z = yellow   K = red   q = purple

THE
SAILING
SAINT

Name

Copy the sentence then draw a picture to illustrate it.

Brendan was a

sailing saint.

SPELLING TEST 2

1. _____

2. _____

3. _____

4. _____

5. _____

6. _____

7. _____

8. _____

9. _____

10. _____

*E A and E E/Operate a partnership/Though one might
be silent/Said together they sound just the same/
You find them sounding "E"/Like in SEED, FEED,
EAT/Their GUARANTEED to always sound like ____*

A I and letters A Y/Put together make the sound of a
LONG _____/A I and A Y are in so many words/
Such as PAID, AIDE, SAY, and HAY/
Food the horses eat!

Name   *Hearing*

REVIEW

INSTRUCTIONS:
Circle the squares blue that have the sound of long A.
Circle the squares red that have the sound of long O.
Circle the squares yellow that have the sound of long I.

Name

REVIEW

INSTRUCTIONS:
Next to each letter write the matching lower or upper case letter.

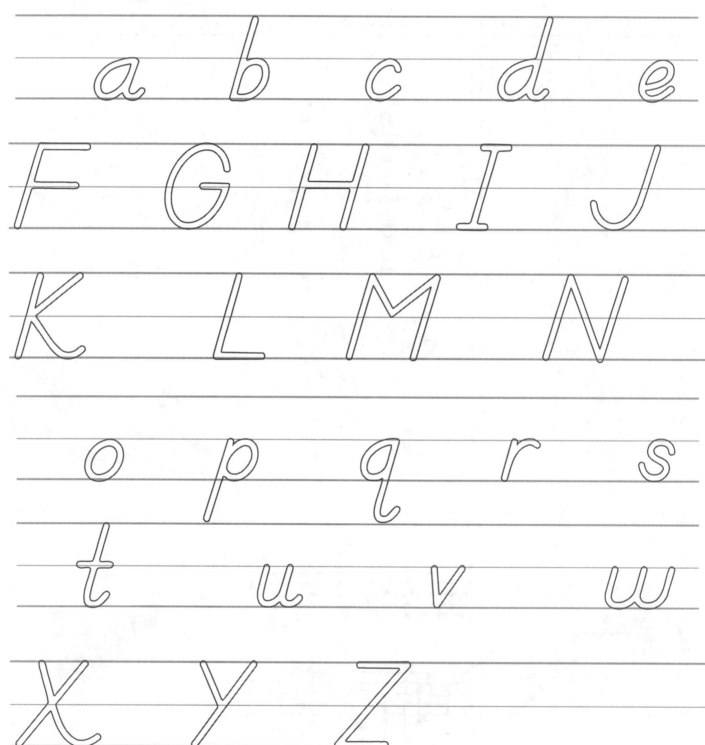

REVIEW

INSTRUCTIONS:
Say each word then circle the beginning sound for each picture.

fr · br 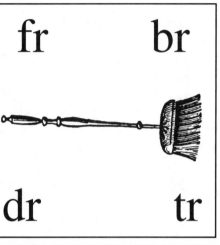 dr · tr	fr · br  dr · tr	fr · br  dr · tr
fr · br  dr · tr	fr · br  dr · tr	fr · br  dr · tr
fr · br  dr · tr	fr · br  dr · tr	fr · br  dr · tr

REVIEW

Name

INSTRUCTIONS:
Cut out the pictures below and glue them in the correct boxes.

horse	hand	bike	dish
wheel	dress	blade	wagon

 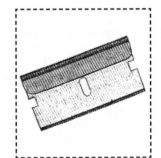  

  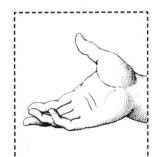 

207

REVIEW

Name

sun	pig	land
man	den	let
fun	cot	doll
red	sick	bill
not	rock	tell
gun	pack	hit
bed	duck	hat
top	neck	sand
bat	tuck	send

REVIEW

INSTRUCTIONS:
Read up and down the word columns.

dump	desk	shall
dent	luck	shut
tent	bump	shock
nest	win	shut
rest	wind	rush
hand	wet	mash
best	will	dish
milk	went	
self	shell	

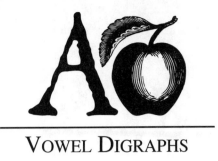

VOWEL DIGRAPHS

Name

INSTRUCTIONS:
Copy the sentence in your best handwriting then draw
a picture to illustrate it.

The green tree
sways in the
breeze.

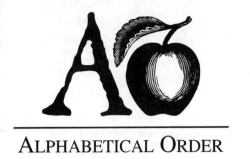

ALPHABETICAL ORDER

INSTRUCTIONS:
INSTRUCTIONS:
Place the following words in alphabetical order. When you are alphabetizing words and they begin with the same letter you must look at the second letter to put them in order.

A B C D E F G H I J K L M N O P Q R S T U V W X Y Z

bat bed big

1. _____

2. _____

3. _____

set sin sun

1. _____

2. _____

3. _____

top ten tan

1. _____

2. _____

3. _____

pig peg pan

1. _____

2. _____

3. _____

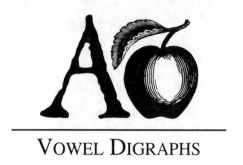

VOWEL DIGRAPHS

_____
Name

INSTRUCTIONS:
Circle the correct answers to the sentences below.

1. Dan went to swim at the _____.

    BEACH   PRAISE   SHEET

2. Jan put butter on her _____.

    HAIR   BREAD   FEET

3. The color of the frog is _____.

    GREEN   SWEEP   STEEP

4. The mama horse had a baby_____.

    BEACH   BOAT   FOAL

5. I _____ in my bed.

    FEAST   TREE   SLEEP

6. The mother _____ had baby cubs.

    JEEP   FISH   BEAR

7. The _____ was in the field of corn.

    STAIN   DEER   TOAST

8. My Dad drives a _____.

    FOAM   JEEP   BEAR

COMPREHENSION

INSTRUCTIONS:
Color the bear black. Color the leaves on the tree green.
Color the trunk of the tree tan. Color the frog green. Color
the horse and the foal gray. Color the goat white.

COMPOUND WORDS

INSTRUCTIONS:
When we add numbers together they form new numbers like 2+2=4. When we add words together they form new words like tea+pot=teapot. Add the words below to make these new words that we call *compound words*.

1. sail + boat = _____

2. gold + fish = _____

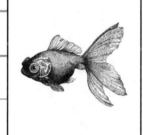

3. base + ball = _____

4. mail + box = _____

INSTRUCTIONS:
Match the words on the left with the pictures on the right.
There are more words than pictures.

crying

reading

falling

fishing

jumping

smiling

drumming

sleeping

219

SPELLING LIST 3

_____
Name

INSTRUCTIONS:
Copy the words below.

brain

grain

say

stay

creek

A I and letters A Y/Put together make the sound of a LONG A/A I and A Y are in so many words/
Such as PAID, AIDE, SAY, and HAY/Food the horses eat!

SPELLING LIST 3

INSTRUCTIONS:
Copy the words below.

beach

heat

roam

float

crow

*E A and E E/Operate a partnership/Though one might be silent/Said together they sound just the same/
You find them sounding "E"/Like in SEED, FEED, EAT/Their GUARANTEED to always sound like "E"*

Name

REVIEW

INSTRUCTIONS:
Write the correct letter on each line to complete the word.
Then copy the word on the lines provided.

d ___ ck

f ___ x

c ___ t

c ___ p

f ___ sh

Name

REVIEW

INSTRUCTIONS:
Write the correct letter on each line to complete the word.
Then copy the word on the lines provided.

k te

b ll

fl te

d me

n se

Name

REVIEW

INSTRUCTIONS:
In your best handwriting copy the sentence below then color the picture.

The red plane flies in the air.

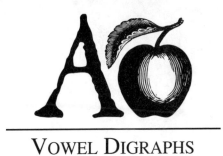

VOWEL DIGRAPHS

INSTRUCTIONS:
Read up and down the word columns.

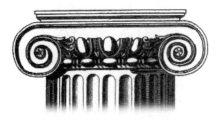

home	boat	family
loves	sweep	husband
hopes	rain	Grandmother
bakes	trains	find
safe	hears	most
Dave	saints	says
faith	day	only
coat	prays	lives
streaks	oaths	Ruth
hair	teaches	God
glean	wise	Lexi
grain	leak	Naomi
read	Mommy	
beams	Daddy	

LEXI'S HOPE

INSTRUCTIONS:
Match the words on the left to the pictures on the right.
There are more words than pictures.

bread

tea

pie

cake

butter

wheat

pear

beef

peach

LEXI'S HOPE

INSTRUCTIONS:
Circle the correct answers to the sentences below.

1. Lexi's mother teaches her to _____.

    SKIP   PRINT   BAKE

2. Lexi likes to paint _____.

    HAY   BREAD   FEET

3. Lexi and her Grandmother bake _____.

    BREAD   STONES   BIBLES

4. Daddy teaches Lexi to hope in God's _____.

    TOES   OATH   HAND

5. Lexi likes to read of _____.

    TREES   BUGS   SAINTS

6. God put a _____ in the sky to show his oath.

    BOW   FISH   BEARS

7. Only _____ can make Lexi wise.

    DOGS   GOD   TOAST

LEXI'S HOPE

INSTRUCTIONS:
In red crayon circle the things that Lexi painted, in a blue crayon the things she baked, and cross out in a green crayon things that were not in the story.

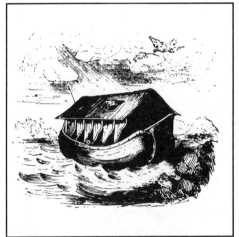
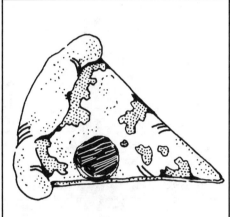

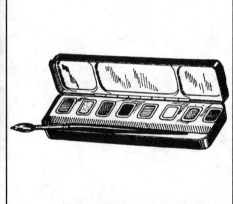

231

LEXI'S HOPE

INSTRUCTIONS:
Give students a large piece of finger painting paper and small amounts of finger paint. Have them paint the rainbow from the story, reminding them of its meaning.

OO

When O is doubled in a word it makes two different sounds as in *moon* and *good*.
INSTRUCTIONS:
Circle the double O in each word.

good	bloom	hood
cool	groom	stood
zoo	troop	wood
doom	look	wool
stool	took	moon
soon	brook	tool

There are twins who look *exactly the same. They appear as OO, and Double O is their name. When they speak you hear a short or long U; The short one says* good *and the long one says* zoo.

233

OO

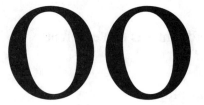

Name

INSTRUCTIONS:
Circle the squares in blue that have pictures with the double O sound in them.

  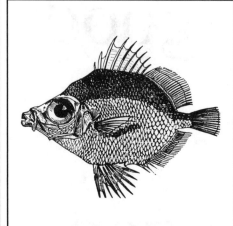

 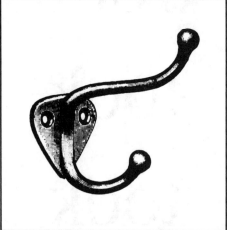 

SPELLING TEST 3

A I and letters A Y/Put together make the sound of a LONG _____/A I and A Y are in so many words/ Such as PAID, AIDE, SAY, and HAY/Food the horses eat!

SPELLING TEST 3

*E A and E E/Operate a partnership/Though one might be silent/Said together they sound just the same/
You find them sounding "E"/Like in SEED, FEED, EAT/Their GUARANTEED to always sound like _____*

Name

OO

INSTRUCTIONS:
When we put the pieces of a puzzle together it makes a picture. When we put letters together they make words.

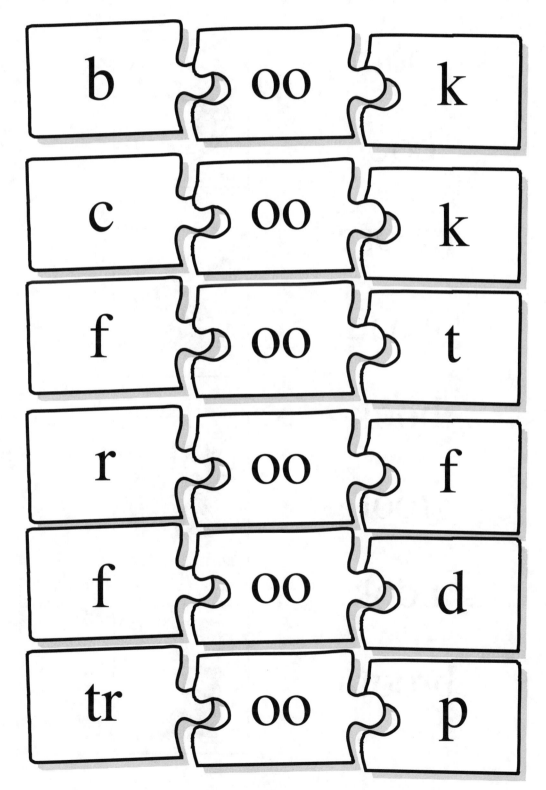

b oo k

c oo k

f oo t

r oo f

f oo d

tr oo p

237

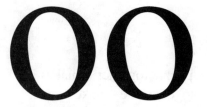

INSTRUCTIONS:
Match the words on the left to the pictures on the right.
There are more words than pictures.

tooth

boot

moose

woad

book

foot

hook

broom

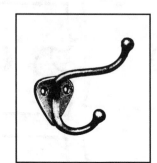

INSTRUCTIONS:
Read up and down the word columns.

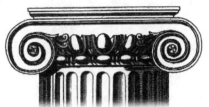  

took	spooky	loose
tools	looming	roof
boot	hood	nook
moon	too	good
scoop	hoop	mood
brook	shoot	
cool	loop	

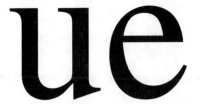

The letters UE together make the long U sound that you hear in the word *blue*.

INSTRUCTIONS:

Circle the letter pair UE in each word.

blue   due

true   cue

glue   rue

hue   Sue

Long U, long U do you have a friend? Yes sir, E is with me to the end. We cannot separate;
We stick together like glue. *You could search until you're* blue *and never find a friend so* true!
(To the tune of Baa, Baa Black Sheep)

The letters UE together make the long U sound that you hear in the word *blue*.

INSTRUCTIONS:

Circle the letter pair UE in each word.

news   grew

dew   blew

few   screw

crew   chew

stew

E and W live very far apart; So when they get together, they catch up on the news.
While together, EW says long U to make up words like grew *and* blew *and* stew.

ew/ue

INSTRUCTIONS:

When we put the pieces of a puzzle together it makes a
picture. When we put letters together they make words.

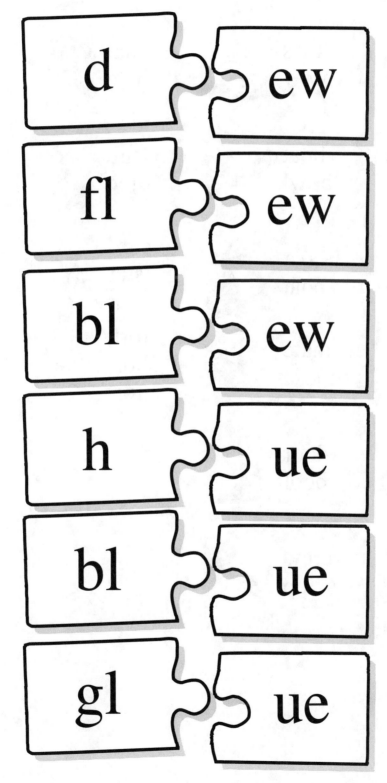

243

Name _____

TEST

INSTRUCTIONS:
Circle the correct answer.

soap
slow

toes
row

hat
hate

dim
dime

window
yellow

boat
bowl

tub
tube

tap
tape

goes
goat

coat
boat

card
star
car

far
car
jar

mow
moon

mate
moose

fork
short
fort

bird
burn
farm

books
bike

door
boot

hum
hook

screw
scrap

244

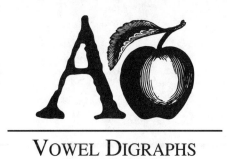

Vowel Digraphs

INSTRUCTIONS:
Read up and down the word columns.

door	behind	croon
floor	Mr.	Ka-Doom
moor	anything	ray
boot	noose	loon
scoop	ooze	rue
looming	brew	unhooking
gloom	rescue	strobe
loose	China	swoon
doom	goo	self-destruct
stoop	spew	mooring
troops	swooping	nearby
brood	flue	sloop
snoop	pursue	anchor
beheld	nook	

RED HOOD

INSTRUCTIONS:
Draw a line to connect the descriptions with the characters in the story.

From China

Had a Ka-Doom Ray

Set the Ka-Doom Ray to self-destruct

Used a hoop to trap his enemy

Used a strobe to blind his enemy

Did not escape on a boat

Put a pack by the stream to cool

RED HOOD

INSTRUCTIONS:
Place a check by the correct answers to the
questions below.

1. What did the Spy use to fly?
____ a plane
____ a bird
____ a pack on his back
____ rockets on his feet

2. Who was the evil man?
____ Red Hood
____ Sue Woo
____ Robin Hood
____ Kung Fu

3. What did the gum do?
____ It made a big bubble
____ It ate up the lock
____ It stuck to the bad man's feet
____ It cut the rope

4. How did the Spy and the girl get away?
____ on a rocket
____ in a jet
____ on a boat
____ in the Spy's car

RED HOOD

INSTRUCTIONS:
Circle the correct answers to the sentences below.

1. From the back of his car the Spy took out _____.

    FOOD   WOOD   TOOLS

2. The pack blew smoke and fire from a scoop and

    soon the Spy _____.

        FLEW   RAN   SAT

3. The Spy met a woman by the name of _____.

    BLUE FLEW   SUE WOO   KIM CHEW

4. The name of Red Hood's weapon was _____.

    KA-DOOM RAY   GUM GUN   THE ZOOMER

5. Place the pictures below in order by placing a

    number under each box

RED HOOD

Name

INSTRUCTIONS:
The illustrations for the story *Red Hood* are inspired by Soviet posters of the past that were made for movies and the theater. In the space below create a movie poster for *Red Hood* using only red, white, black and yellow.

England's Best Spy stars in:
RED HOOD

oi/oy

Name

INSTRUCTIONS:
Color the boxes blue that have pictures that have the sound of OI or OY.

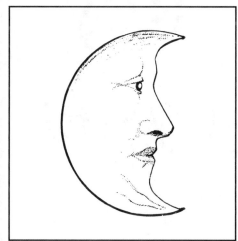

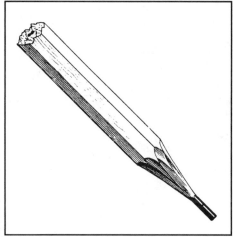

oi/oy

Name

Worksheet 82B
Seeing

INSTRUCTIONS:
Circle the "oi" or the "oy" in the words below.

boil	spoil	coy
coin	toil	soy
join	boy	Roy
noise	joy	oyster
point	toy	

oi/oy

INSTRUCTIONS:
Read up and down the word columns.

oil	join	soy
boil	foil	coy
toil	point	boys
soil	boy	toys
coin	toy	joys
coil	joy	oyster

oi/oy

Name

Worksheet 83B
Writing

INSTRUCTIONS:
Copy the OI/OY words below.

boy

joy

toy

noise

spoil

coin

oi/oy

INSTRUCTIONS:
Match the word on the left to the correct picture on
the right. There are more words than pictures.

boys

toil

oysters

boil

foil

toys

coins

257

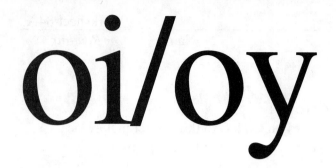

INSTRUCTIONS:
Circle the word that completes each sentence.

1. Jan _____ the water to make tea.

     SOIL   BOILS   TOYS

2. The _____ like to play baseball.

     COINS   OYSTERS   BOYS

3. Dad said we were making too much _____ .

     NOISE   HOIST   BOY

4. The _____ is rich and good for plants.

     SOIL   JOY   NOISE

5. We got _____ at the beach.

     VOICE   PAINT   OYSTERS

6. Jack likes the _____ he got on his birthday.

     POINTS   JOY   TOYS

7. Mom wraps the meat in _____ .

     HATS   FOIL   SOY

8. My Dad puts _____ in the car.

     OIL   POINT   VOICE

oi/oy

Name

INSTRUCTIONS:
In your best handwriting copy the sentence below then color the picture.

The boys play with their toys.

259

Name

INSTRUCTIONS:
Color the shapes following the guide at the bottom.

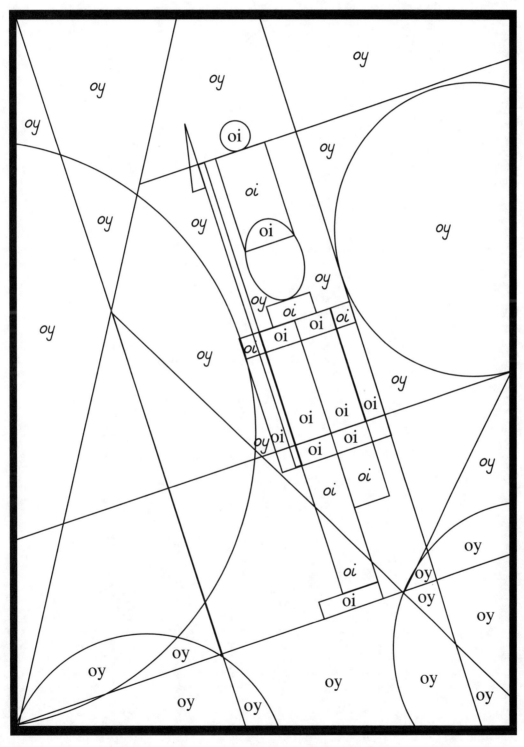

oi = red oy = blue *oi* = purple *oy* = yellow

261

REVIEW

INSTRUCTIONS
Choose from the following blends and fill in the missing beginning letter pairs for each word (BL, FL, TR, GR, CR, FR, DR). Then copy each word on the lines.

um

apes

ag

og

oom

263

Name

REVIEW

INSTRUCTIONS

Say each picture. Write the letter that stands for the ending sound of each picture.

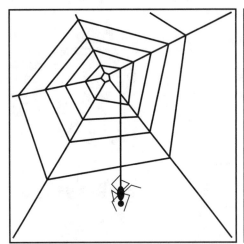

oi/oy

INSTRUCTIONS:
Read up and down the word columns. Circle those words that are OI/OY.

bake	pray	horn
boil	boil	coin
cake	toys	point
coil	hike	park
ride	boy	soil
rope	joy	join
dime	jump	

SPELLING LIST 4

INSTRUCTIONS:
Copy the OI/OY words below.

oil

coil

coin

soil

join

boy

joy

toy

coy

soy

REVIEW

Name

INSTRUCTIONS:
Color the circles green that have the sound of IR.

Name

INSTRUCTIONS:
Write the sentence in your best handwriting, then complete
and color the picture.

*The boys hoist the toy
into the tree.*

_____
Name

REVIEW

INSTRUCTIONS:
Someone came into the museum and scrambled the letters for the name plates. Match the picture to its mixed-up partner then write out the word beside the picture.

tab

cpu

deb

snu

tac

oi/oy

INSTRUCTIONS:
Read up and down the word columns.

Roy	Sir Galahad	marshes
moist	King Arthur	quest
join	Lord	Holy Grail
toying	Sir Bors	fret
foil	Hydra	neglecting
hoisting	fishing	brutal
toiling	digging	loin
boiling	pulling	blood
joints	looking	spoils
spoils	booming	nay
choice	thrusting	farewell
noise	turning	

Name *Comprehension*

A Tale of Sir Galahad

INSTRUCTIONS:
After reading *A Tale of Sir Galahad,* circle the
correct answers to the questions below.

1. When Galahad met Roy, the boy was _____.

   SINGING   FISHING   SLEEPING

2. Where did Sir Bors get lost?

   WOODS   MARSHES   HILLS

3. What did King Arthur send his men on a
   quest to find?

   SILVER   MONKS   GRAIL

4. What was living over the hill by Roy?

   CATS   HYDRA   NIX

5. Roy threw a _____ to help Galahad.

   DOG   HAT   NET

6. What did Roy offer Galahad to stay there?

   SPOILS   FOOD   WINE

A TALE OF
SIR GALAHAD

INSTRUCTIONS:
After reading *A Tale of Sir Galahad*, recreate some of the strange fish or perhaps even the hydra using the sand dough receipe below.

SUPPLIES:
Ingredients:
4 cups sand
2 cups cornstarch
1 tbl + 1 tsp Cream of Tartar
3 cups hot water

INSTRUCTIONS:
Mix sand, cornstarch and cream of tartar in large saucepan. Stir in hot water. Cook over medium heat, stirring constantly until water is absorbed and mixture is too stiff to stir. Cool until it can be handled.

Store in airtight container—air dries in a few days.

ou/ow

INSTRUCTIONS:
Color the boxes brown that have pictures that have the sound of OU or OW as in *out*.

273

ou/ow

Name

Worksheet 90B
Seeing

INSTRUCTIONS:
Circle the OU or OW in the words below as in *out* or *cow.*

out	round	plow
house	scout	howl
count	how	flower
found	down	cow
pound	brown	
ground	crown	

SPELLING TEST 4

1.

2.

3.

4.

5.

6.

7.

8.

9.

10.

INSTRUCTIONS:
Read up and down the word columns. Circle those words that contain OU/OW.

 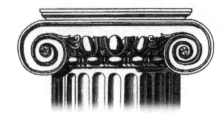 

our	Howard	browse
bound	town	scouting
out	crowd	route
hour	fallow	prow
house	mow	scowl
flour	window	dousing
count	bows	snout
countess	arrows	coward
cloudy	flowing	drowsy
crouch	grouse	

ou/ow

INSTRUCTIONS:
Match the word on the left to the correct picture
on the right. There are more words than pictures.

couch

flower

house

mouse

mouth

cow

gown

mound

SPELLING LIST 5

INSTRUCTIONS:
Copy the OU/OW words below.

out

house

about

shout

mouse

how

clown

brown

now

flower

The Phonic rule for O U O W / They sound the same though/ The spelling is different
But now you know O U and O W/ They make the sound of OW!

HOWARD SAVES
A HOUND

INSTRUCTIONS:
After reading *Howard Saves a Hound,* fill in the circle for
the correct answers to the questions below.

1. Why is Howard happy about this hunt?
   - ○ It is the first of the season.
   - ○ It is his first hunt.
   - ○ Howard gets to shoot a bow and arrow.
2. What is Father's job?
   - ○ Count
   - ○ boat man
   - ○ Master of the hounds
3. For what do they hunt that day?
   - ○ fallow
   - ○ deer
   - ○ foxes
4. How did the hounds get across the river?
   - ○ on a log
   - ○ by swimming
   - ○ by boat
5. For what did Father praise Howard?
   - ○ bravery
   - ○ swimming ability
   - ○ wisdom

HOWARD SAVES A HOUND

INSTRUCTIONS:
Cut out the squares on the right side of the paper. Read each of the "Cause" sentences on the left side of the paper. Glue the "Effect" squares you cut out by its "Cause."

The men see the Countess.

Howard is cold from being in the river.

Howard thinks the hound needs help.

The boat tips when Father gets out.

Father praises Howard.

Father builds a fire.

The men smile.

Howard glows with pride.

A hound falls in the water.

Howard jumps in the water.

ou/ow

Name

INSTRUCTIONS:
Write the sentence in your best handwriting, and color the picture.

The brown mouse runs over the mound.

HOWARD SAVES A HOUND

Name

INSTRUCTIONS:
Make a pack of hunting hounds using your fingerprints!

SOFT C

Name

INSTRUCTIONS:
Circle the CE or CI in the words below.

ⓒⓔnt   cider   race

cell   cinder   rice

center   ace   prince

civil   place   fence

---

1. If the letter "C" is used before e, i, or y it has the sound of "s."
2. "Ce" at the end of a word has the sound of "S."
3. "Ce" directly after a vowel tells us the vowel is long.
4. "Ci" or "cy" says "si."

ce=se   ci=si   cy=si

287

SOFT C

INSTRUCTIONS:
Color the boxes purple that have pictures that have the sound of soft C in either the beginning, middle or the end of the word.

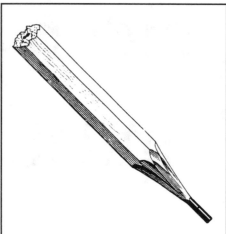

SOFT C

Name

INSTRUCTIONS:
Read up and down the word columns.

cent	lace	price
center	ice	fence
cell	spice	since
ace	rice	cycle

SOFT C

INSTRUCTIONS:
In your best handwriting copy the sentence below, then illustrate it.

The mice prance on the fence.

SOFT C

INSTRUCTIONS:
Match the word on the left to the correct picture on the right. There are more words than pictures.

lace

ice cream

mice

pencil

prince

fence

rice

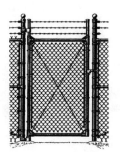

SPELLING TEST 5

1. _____

2. _____

3. _____

4. _____

5. _____

6. _____

7. _____

8. _____

9. _____

10. _____

The Phonic rule for O U O W / They sound the same though/ The spelling is different
But now you know O U and O W/ They make the sound of _____!

SOFT C

_____

Name

INSTRUCTIONS:
Circle the word that completes each sentence.

1. The _____ wore a crown.

      PRINCE   PEACE   SPACE

2. The _____ like cheese.

      MICE   TWICE   SPACE

3. I want a _____ of pie.

      PIECE   PENCIL   RACE

4. The boys ran in a _____ .

      RICE   LACE   RACE

5. Jan likes _____ in her drink.

      ICE   MICE   FACE

6. Jim ate a _____ of an apple.

      CENT   DANCE   SLICE

7. Brandon writes with a _____ .

      CENT   CIGAR   PENCIL

8. The children went to the _____ to see
the animals.

      PEACE   CIRCUS   PRICE

SPELLING LIST 6

INSTRUCTIONS:
Copy the silent C words below.

mice

race

cent

ice

face

nice

mince

space

dance

price

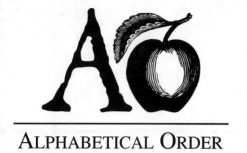

ALPHABETICAL ORDER

Name

INSTRUCTIONS:
Place the following words in alphabetical order. When you are alphabetizing words and they begin with the same letter, you must look at the second letter to put them in order.

A B C D E F G H I J K L M N O P Q R S T U V W X Y Z

cent nice ice face

1. _____

2. _____

3. _____

4. _____

mince fence
center hence

1. _____

2. _____

3. _____

4. _____

pace piece
dance mice

1. _____

2. _____

3. _____

4. _____

SOFT C

INSTRUCTIONS:
In your best handwriting copy the
sentence below then color the picture.

The prince went to France.

SOFT C

INSTRUCTIONS:
Draw a line from the words on the left to the words on the right which have the same letter pairs in the same positions.

CE=SE CI=SI CY=SI

cent   cyclops

city   race

lace   cell

cyclone   cinder

REVIEW

Name

Say the name of each picture. Write the correct
middle sound for each word.

h t

f sh

p n

c p

t p

298

TEST

INSTRUCTIONS:
Circle the correct answer.

toil
toy

oysters
oil

boys
bows

boil
boss

boot
but

glut
goose

moon
moan

ringer
rooster

must
moose

crown
croon

cow
cud

flog
flower

hope
hook

huff
house

miss
mouse

mouth
mine

towel
owl

books
brooks

fence
fast

cigar
sift

broom
loom

poor
pencil

most
mice

last
lace

bear
back

SOFT C

INSTRUCTIONS:
Color the boxes green that have the sound of hard C, color the boxes orange that have the sound of soft C.

cat

lace

cup

fence

prince

car

dice

cards

mice

Soft C

Name

INSTRUCTIONS
Write the correct word under each picture from the
following list: fence, ice, dice, dance, lace, mice,
spaceship, pencil, cent

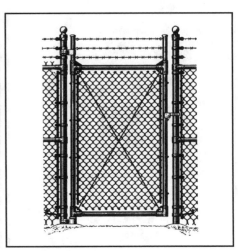

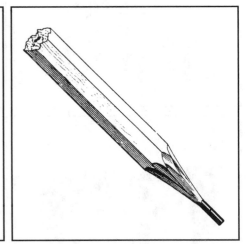

ING

Name

INSTRUCTIONS
Write the correct word ending to the words below to
match the picture.

box

crawl

sled

rain

sow

303

Name

REVIEW

INSTRUCTIONS:
Color the boxes orange where you hear the short sound of E and color the boxes yellow where you hear the long sound of E.

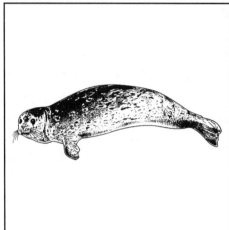

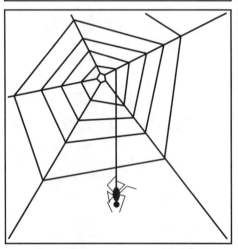

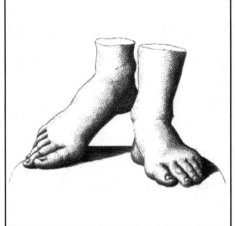

ou/ow

Name

Worksheet 103A
Writing

INSTRUCTIONS:
Circle the OUL in each word and place a backslash through the L. Then copy the sentences in the spaces provided.

should

could

would

Should the prince play cards?

Could the mice roll dice?

Would the cat hold the lace?

SOFT C

INSTRUCTIONS:
Read up and down the word columns.

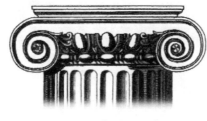

wind	voices	straining
brisk	piece	bouncing
armor	steel	tracing
bracing	mail	lacing
racing	lace	wincing
England	pacing	space
prince	since	cease
pounce	face	prizes
trounce	grace	empty
could	price	center
would	survive	dancing
pope	prancing	hence
Rome	female	choice
kingdom	Spain	Scotland
Elizabeth	slicing	stance

SPELLING TEST 6

1.

2.

3.

4.

5.

6.

7.

8.

9.

10.

Soft C

Name

INSTRUCTIONS:
Cut out pictures from magazines that have the sound of soft C and use them to create a collage.

QUEEN
OF THE SEA

INSTRUCTIONS:
After reading *Queen of the Sea*, circle the correct
answers to the questions below.

1. Who was the queen of the sea?

QUEEN MARY   QUEEN ELIZABETH   QUEEN ANN

2. Of what land was she queen?

SPAIN   FRANCE   ENGLAND

3. Who came to attack the queen of the sea?

THE PRINCE OF SPAIN

THE DUKE OF WALES

THE KING OF FRANCE

4. Why did he want to defeat the queen?

TO GET BACK AT HER

TO TAKE BACK HIS LAND

TO GIVE HER LAND A PRINCE WHO WOULD LOVE THE POPE

5. What did the queen promise her men?

THEY WOULD GET LAND IF THEY WON.

SHE WOULD STAY WITH THEM.

SHE WOULD PAY THEM MORE.

6. Which ships were faster?

ENGLISH   FRENCH   SPANISH

7. Which fleet won the battle?

ENGLAND   FRANCE   SPAIN

QUEEN OF THE SEA

INSTRUCTIONS:
Make a boat to help the English navy!

Using a half gallon or quart milk carton students can make boats that will actually float. Below is a copy of the English flag that students may color, cut out, and glue to a popsicle stick for the top of their boat. A simple boat plan would be to have students paint their milk carton and poke their popsicle stick flag into the top of the boat. You may wish to give them some ideas and let them try to come up with their own design. They may wish to cut away part of the carton, put rolled up pieces of paper cannons on the deck, or make sails from paper and popsicle sticks. Whatever you do, be sure to test them out on the high seas (bath tub, swimming pool, or lake).

AW / AU / AL

Name

INSTRUCTIONS:
Circle the AW/AU/AL in the words below.

saw	sauce	wall
jaw	pause	hall
paw	cause	tall
law	faucet	talk
draw	ball	walk
yawn	call	stalk
fawn	fall	balk

Aw / Au / Al

Name

INSTRUCTIONS:
Color the boxes blue where you hear the sound of AW. It may be spelled AU, AW or AL but you only have to listen for the sound AW.

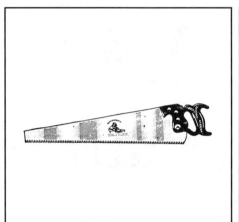

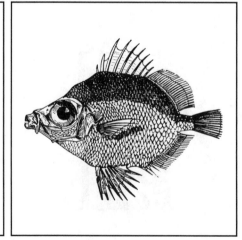

Aw / Au / Al

INSTRUCTIONS:
Read up and down the word columns.

saw	lawn	call
jaw	yawn	tall
paw	haul	talk
law	sauce	walk
draw	cause	chalk
fawn	flaunt	stalk
straw	fault	
raw	ball	

SPELLING LIST 7

INSTRUCTIONS:
Copy the AW/AU/AL words below.

ball

tall

call

hall

saw

paw

lawn

haul

auto

cause

The phonic rule BROAD O SOUND/ Is made by A and L "like in CALL"/ And if you see both A and W
It should sound so AWFUL/ Sometimes you'll see A followed by U/ And AUTOMATICALLY know/
That you are using the Phonic rule/ The Phonic Rule BROAD O

AW / AU / AL

INSTRUCTIONS:
Match the word on the left to the correct picture
on the right. There are more words than pictures.

crawl

ball

fawn

straw

saw

haul

sauce

wall

319

Aw / Au / Al

INSTRUCTIONS:
Read up and down the word columns.

   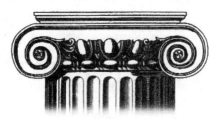

awful	lawn	haunt
raw	calling	Claudius
dawn	small	daunt
shawl	also	paunch
brawny	balk	Maud
drawn	animals	haunches
straw	small	yawn
draw	because	bawl
saw	staunch	jaunt
flaws	haul	cawing
brawling	Aurelius	fawn
claws	squalid	reminding
paws	gaunt	
jaws	fault	

Name

SILENT CONSONANTS

INSTRUCTIONS:
Circle the KN, GN or WR in the words below, then put a line through the silent partner.

knot gnaw wrong

knee write wretch

kneel wring knife

knit wren wreath

knob wreck wrench

knock wrist gnome

gnat wrote

In some words two consonants have one sound, just like the silent partners we already have studied. Look at the examples below.

kn as in *knot*—we only hear the sound of n
gn as in *gnat*—we only hear the sound of n
wr as in *write*—we only hear the sound of r

SILENT CONSONANTS

Name

INSTRUCTIONS:
Circle the correct silent consonant for each picture.

kn gn wr	kn gn wr	kn gn wr

kn gn
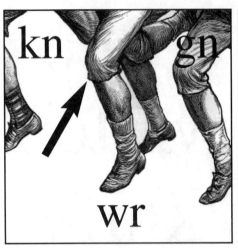
wr

kn gn
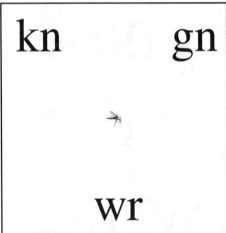
wr

kn gn

wr

kn gn
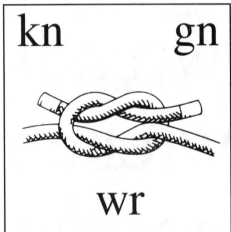
wr

kn gn

wr

kn gn

wr

kn gn

wr

kn gn

wr

kn gn

wr

SILENT CONSONANTS

Name

INSTRUCTIONS:
Color in the picture below using the key at the bottom of the page.

K = red G = blue W = gold

Silent Consonants

INSTRUCTIONS:
Read up and down the word columns.

knot	knelt	write
knack	knife	wrong
knead		wretch
knee	write	wreath
know	wring	wrung
known	wren	
knock	wrist	gnat
knob	wrote	gnaw

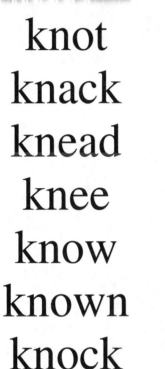   

SILENT CONSONANTS

Name

INSTRUCTIONS:
Circle the GH, MB, LF, LK, or TLE in the words below,
then put a line through the silent partner.

sigh	calf	lamb
night	half	Knight
bright	castle	thumb
light	rustle	comb
fight	dumb	whistle
high	plumb	

In some words two consonants have one sound, just like the silent partners we already have studied. Look at the examples below.

lf as in *calf*—we only hear the sound of F
gh as in *right*—we only hear the sound of T
mb as in *lamb*—we only hear the sound of M
lk as in *walk*—we only hear the sound of K
tle as in *castle*—we only hear the sound of L

SILENT CONSONANTS

INSTRUCTIONS:
Circle the correct consonant group for each picture.

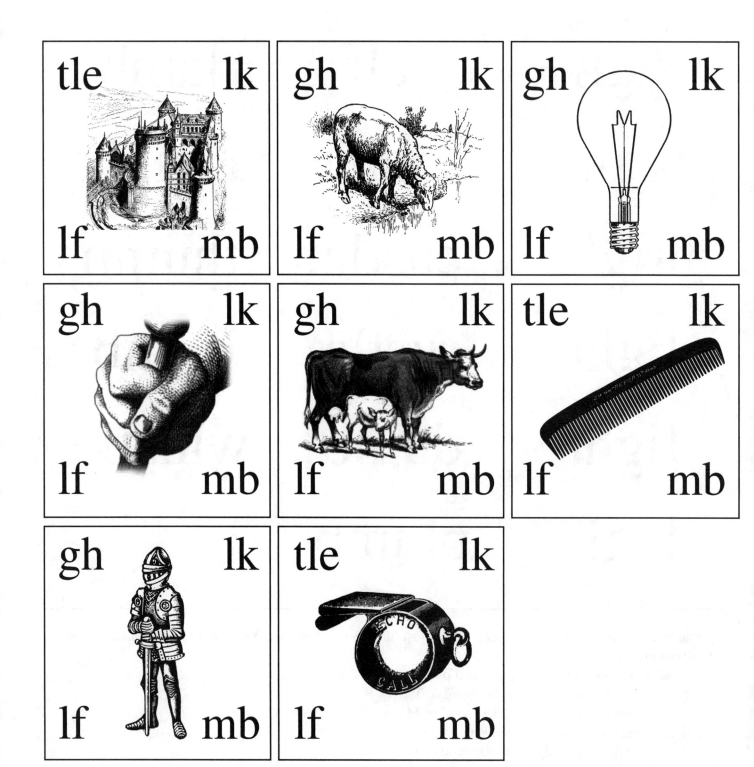

SILENT CONSONANTS

INSTRUCTIONS:
Match the word on the left to the correct picture on the right.

wrist

calf

lamb

gnat

knot

wreath

knife

comb

knight

knee

Silent Consonants

INSTRUCTIONS:
Read up and down the word columns.

sigh	high	dumb
sight	knight	plumb
tight	calf	limb
night	half	lamb
bright	castle	numb
fight	hustle	
light	bustle	

SPELLING TEST 7

1.

2.

3.

4.

5.

6.

7.

8.

9.

10.

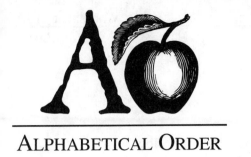

ALPHABETICAL ORDER

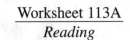

Name   *Reading*

INSTRUCTIONS:
Place the following words in alphabetical order. When you are alphabetizing words and they begin with the same letter, you must look at the third letter to put them in order.

A B C D E F G H I J K L M N O P Q R S T U V W X Y Z

lamb bomb numb
dumb comb

1. _____

2. _____

3. _____

4. _____

5. _____

knee knit knack
knob knot

1. _____

2. _____

3. _____

4. _____

5. _____

SPELLING LIST 8

Name

INSTRUCTIONS:
Copy the silent consonant words below.

knot

knee

gnat

gnaw

write

wrong

sigh

bright

lamb

climb

lf as in *calf*—we only hear the sound of _____ /   gh as in *right*—we only hear the sound of _____ /
mb as in *lamb*—we only hear the sound of _____ / lk as in *walk*—we only hear the sound of _____ /
tle as in *castle*—we only hear the sound of _____

SILENT CONSONANTS

INSTRUCTIONS:
Circle the word that completes each sentence.

1. The other sheep had a baby _____ .

    COMB   LAMB   BOMB

2. Pam was _____ a sweater.

    KNOWING   KNEELING   KNITTING

3. The boys are _____ the tree.

    CLIMBING   LAMB   THUMB

4. The girls took a _____ down the path.

    KNIT   KNEE   WALK

5. Jan was _____ her hair.

    COMBING   BOMBING   CLIMBING

6. There is a _____ in the rope.

    CLIMB   KNOT   KNACK

7. I can _____ my own name.

    LAMB   PLUMBING   WRITE

8. Jim uses a _____ to spread his butter.

    KNOW   KNIFE   KNACK

SILENT CONSONANTS

Name

INSTRUCTIONS:
Cut out pictures from magazines that have silent consonants and use them to create a collage (ex. knight, light, lamb).

SILENT CONSONANTS

Name

INSTRUCTIONS:
Copy the silent consonant words below.

I ought to have brought the thing I bought.

SILENT CONSONANTS

INSTRUCTIONS:
Write the sentence in your best handwriting,
then illustrate it.

The knights fight at the castle.

SILENT CONSONANTS

INSTRUCTIONS:
Read up and down the word columns.

night	high	crumb
slight	straight	numb
taught	gnomes	wrench
knights	Anne	poem
fights	Bradstreet	rime
frights	England	fraught
sigh	Simon	naught
caught	knead	smallpox
sight	knock	knoll
blight	knack	

BRIGHT
NIGHT

INSTRUCTIONS:
Read each sentence and decide if it happened in the story. Circle the sentences that did happen and cross out the sentences that did not happen.

Anne caught smallpox and was sick.

Anne was in a shipwreck.

Anne went to a far away land.

Anne wrote poems.

Anne was not able to have any children.

Anne was a school teacher.

Anne's house caught on fire.

Anne had faith in God.

Anne's children made a book of her paintings.

Anne was wed when she was sixteen.

BRIGHT NIGHT

INSTRUCTIONS:
After reading *Bright Night,* fill in the blanks with the words from the word bank.

1. Where did Anne grow up? _____

2. What did Anne love to do? _____

3. What disease did Anne have?_____

4. Whom did Anne marry? _____

5. To where did Anne go
   with her husband? _____

6. How did Anne and her husband
   get to their new home? _____

7. What did a fire destroy? _____

Word Bank:

HER SON   NEW ENGLAND   HER HOUSE

SIMON BRADSTREET   ENGLAND

WRITE POEMS   ON A SHIP   SMALLPOX

SILENT CONSONANTS

INSTRUCTIONS:
Write the sentence in your best handwriting.

Anne sought to love God in all she wrote.

The sun is shining,
  The birds are singing
  And my eyes are waking.
  I think of things I'll do today.
There will be
      running and _____,
      laughter and _____,
      books and _____.

The sun is high,
  My friends are here
  And I am _____.
We plan our day's adventures.
We will
      talk and _____,
      make and _____,
      eat and _____.

The moon is high,
  The stars are shining
  My family is giving thanks.
I thank thee good Lord
For
      playmates and _____,
      food and _____,
      books and _____.
And for your Presence always with me.

REVIEW

INSTRUCTIONS:
Circle the correct beginning blend for each picture.

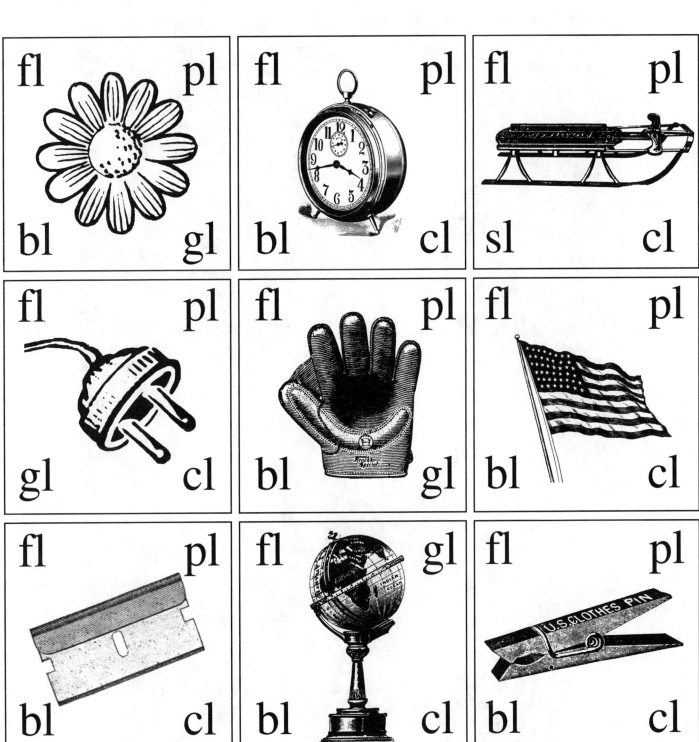

fl		pl
fl		pl
bl		gl

| fl | | pl |
| bl | | cl |

| fl | | pl |
| sl | | cl |

| fl | | pl |
| gl | | cl |

| fl | | pl |
| bl | | gl |

| fl | | pl |
| bl | | cl |

| fl | | pl |
| bl | | cl |

| fl | | gl |
| bl | | cl |

| fl | | pl |
| bl | | cl |

351

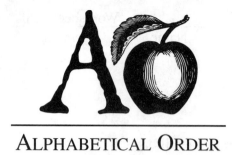

ALPHABETICAL ORDER

Name

Writing

INSTRUCTIONS:
Complete the picture by connecting the dots in alphabetical order.

SPELLING TEST 8

1.

2.

3.

4.

5.

6.

7.

8.

9.

10.

lf as in *calf*—we only hear the sound of _____/ gh as in *right*—we only hear the sound of _____/
mb as in *lamb*—we only hear the sound of _____/   lk as in *walk*—we only hear the sound of _____/
tle as in *castle*—we only hear the sound of _____

J Sound of ge/dge

INSTRUCTIONS:
Match the word on the left to the correct picture on the right. There are more words than pictures.

bridge

hedge

cage

page

judge

fudge

badge

J SOUND OF GE/DGE

INSTRUCTIONS:
Color the boxes purple that have pictures that have the
sound of J made by the GE/DGE letter combination.

356

J Sound of GE/DGE

INSTRUCTIONS:
Read up and down the word columns.

bridge	badge	edge
hedge	cage	fudge
cage	page	ridge
page	age	hedge
judge	rage	bridge
fudge	hinge	

REVIEW

INSTRUCTIONS
Say each picture. Write AR or ER in to complete
each word.

st

c

b n

zipp

hamm

358

Name

TEST

INSTRUCTIONS
Circle the correct answer.

dice
date

lake
lice

knight
kite

lamp
lamb

price
prince

mate
mice

carpet
castle

camp
comb

face
faucet

saw
seen

judge
jump

brick
bridge

bear
barn

crawl
crab

bait
badge

cage
cape

gnat
gnome

knot
coat

walrus
walnut

face
faucet

saint
sauce

bat
ball

dart
dance

cow
cot

mount
mouth

359

J SOUND OF GE/DGE

INSTRUCTIONS:
Read up and down the word columns.

pledge	challenge	damage
diligent	trudge	arrange
charge	voyage	intelligent
barrage	edge	strange
grudge	huge	enrage
large	bridge	
purge	judge	

ALPHABETICAL ORDER

INSTRUCTIONS:
On the lines provided below, write out the entire alphabet in order including both upper and lower case letters.

1.

2.

3.

4.

5.

6.

7.

8.

9.

10.

11.

12.

13.

14.

15.

16.

17.

18.

19.

20.

21.

22.

23.

24.

25.

26.

J Sound of ge/dge

_____
Name

INSTRUCTIONS:
Circle the word that completes each sentence.

1. The man was trimming his _____ .

    BUDGE   LODGE   HEDGE

2. Travis and Brandon made yummy _____ .

    FUDGE   BRIDGE   RIDGE

3. The bird is in its _____ .

    CAGE   SAGE   WAGE

4. Please turn to the next _____ in your book.

    RAGE   CAGE   PAGE

5. When I paid my bill the man gave me _____ .

    HINGE   CHANGE   PLUNGE

6. The play was on the _____ .

    AGE   STAGE   WAGE

7. We took a walk over the _____ .

    FUDGE   DODGE   BRIDGE

8. The window has a _____ on it.

    HUGE   SMUDGE   AGE

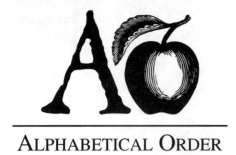

ALPHABETICAL ORDER

INSTRUCTIONS:
Complete the picture by connecting the dots then color.

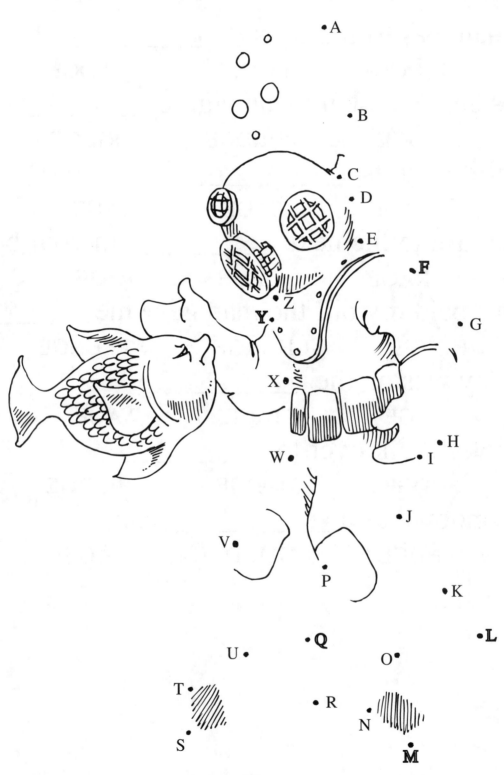

REVIEW

INSTRUCTIONS
Read each word. Circle the vowel pair then write the
sound which the two letters make on the line.

feet _*e*_____

leap _____

tree _____

soak _____

sea _____

coat _____

teach _____

feast _____

week _____

sheet _____

tea _____

loaf _____

toes _____

float _____

keep _____

sweet _____

dream _____

fleet _____

coast _____

J SOUND OF GE/DGE

INSTRUCTIONS:
Write the sentence in your best handwriting.

The cat does not budge when the boy jumps over the hedge.

J Sound of GE/DGE

INSTRUCTIONS:
Circle the GE or GI in the words below, then read them aloud.

gem   germ   margin

gee   gin   tragic

gel   ginger   urgent

gentle   magic

SPELLING LIST 9

INSTRUCTIONS:
Copy the GE/DGE words below.

cage

page

age

rage

hinge

edge

fudge

ridge

hedge

bridge

REVIEW

INSTRUCTIONS:
Say each picture. Write the consonant letter needed to
complete each word.

spoo

fo

ench

bir

ence

J SOUND OF GE/DGE

INSTRUCTIONS:
Read up and down the word columns.

pledge	bridge	Marathon
diligent	judge	enrage
charge	damage	genius
barrage	arrange	important
grudge	intelligent	preparing
large	strange	
purge	archer	
challenge	army	Cyrus
trudge	enemies	very
voyage	weapon	body
edge	arrow	build
huge	battle	two

J Sound of GE/DGE

INSTRUCTIONS:
Write the sentence in your best handwriting.

I am Cyrus, an archer in the army from the East.

CYRUS THE
ARCHER

INSTRUCTIONS:
After reading *Cyrus the Archer,* circle the correct answers to the questions below.

1. What is Cyrus' job?

ARMOR BEARER   MESSENGER   ARCHER

2. What is the main weapon in use by most of the enemies?

SWORDS   SPEARS   GUNS

3. What army are they on their way to attack?

ROME   SPAIN   GREECE

4. What was laid across the boats so the army could walk on them?

BRICKS   ROPES   PLANKS

5. How many days did it take for the army to cross the bridge?

SEVEN   FIVE   TEN

6. What other problem did the army of the East face before they began the attack?

A DESERT   STEEP HILLS   LACK OF FOOD

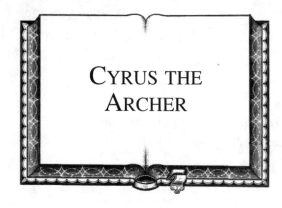

CYRUS THE ARCHER

INSTRUCTIONS:
Build a model bridge.

SUPPLIES:
A large bucket, pot, or bath tub
Paper cups
Popsicle sticks
Yarn or string
Long, thin rocks
Mud or clay
A sewing pin

1. Cut off the tops of the paper cups so that they are only 2" deep. Pinch two opposite sides of the cups so they take on a boat shape.

2. With a pin poke a hole on the top edge of the cups about 1/2" down from the top of the cup and near the middle of the boat. Poke another hole 1/2" down on the opposite side of the cups.

3. Tape the string or yarn to the pin and thread it through the holes in the cups so that they are tied together side by side. Knot both ends of the string.

4. Tie string around the thin rocks and then attach the string to the boats. These are the rock anchors used to steady the boats in the water.

5. Lay three popsicle sticks with middles together. These will be the wooden planks for the bridge. Press the mud or clay onto the sticks. Make enough sets of three so that when placed end to end they will stretch across the row of boats. Mud will have to dry before the popsicle sticks are placed on top of the boat.

6. You may wish to photocopy onto card stock the Persian soldiers and animals at the right, then cut them out to place them on the bridge and/or the two banks.

7. Fill a tub with water and put the bridge in the water.

Name

Reading
Hearing

INSTRUCTIONS:
Say each picture. Circle whether the vowel sound
is short or long.

long a
short a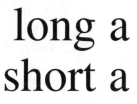

long i
short i

long a
short a

long o
short o

long e
short e

long o
short o

long e
short e

long u
short u

Name

REVIEW

INSTRUCTIONS
Say each picture. Write CH, SH, TH, or WH to complete each word.

_____ell

_____umb

_____ip

_____ale

_____ick

376

TION / SION

Name

TION and SION are pronounced "shun."
INSTRUCTIONS:
Circle the TION or the SION in the words below.

station   section   impression

nation   ignition   mission

creation   celebration   decision

motion   vision   confession

portion   division   pension

SPELLING TEST 9

1.

2.

3.

4.

5.

6.

7.

8.

9.

10.

TION / SION

INSTRUCTIONS:
Color the shapes following the guide at the bottom to complete this vacation picture.

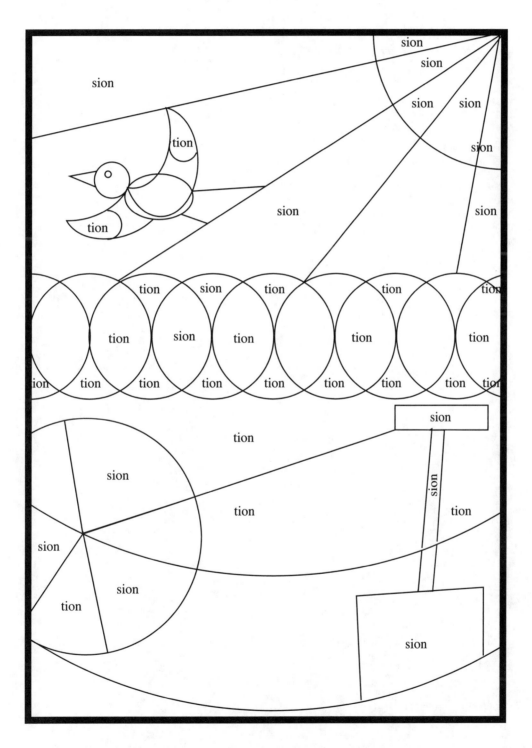

tion = blue   sion = red

379

TION / SION

INSTRUCTIONS:
Read up and down the word columns.

nation	ignition	impression
station	vision	mission
motion	division	session
creation	decision	mansion
portion	confession	passion
section	pension	

TION / SION

INSTRUCTIONS:
Circle the word that completes each sentence.

1. My family is going on a summer _____ .

    HESITATION   VACATION   EXPLOSION

2. Tom Edison made many _____ .

    EXPRESSIONS   INVENTIONS   DIVISIONS

3. I sent out many _____ to the party.

    VACATIONS   POPULATIONS   INVITATIONS

4. Genesis says that the moon was made by God on
    day four of _____ .

    CREATION   EDUCATION   ADDITION

5. I can see my _____ when I look in the puddle.

    NATION   REFLECTION   ADDITION

TION / SION

Name

INSTRUCTIONS:
Write the sentence in your best handwriting.

Genesis says that the moon was made
by God on the fourth day of creation.

Name

REVIEW

INSTRUCTIONS:
Color the circles orange that have pictures that have the sound of OO.

Name

INSTRUCTIONS:

Write the OO words below in the correct list. Do they sound like *moon* or *book*?

SPOON, WOOD, FOOT, HOOK, COOK, BROOM, HOOP, MOOSE

moon

book

INSTRUCTIONS:
Match the blend on the left to the correct picture
on the right. There are more blends than pictures.

bl

fl

cl

tr

br

gr

dr

fr

387

Name

ALPHABETICAL ORDER

A B C D E F G H I J K L M N O P Q R S T U V W X Y Z

action   station   education
vacation   population

1. _____   5. _____

2. _____

3. _____

4. _____

addition   affection   promotion
foundation   mention

1. _____   5. _____

2. _____

3. _____

4. _____

TION / SION

Name

INSTRUCTIONS:
Write the sentence in your best handwriting.

We have an invitation to visit the capitol
of our nation on vacation.

SPELLING LIST 10

INSTRUCTIONS:
Copy the TION/SION words below.

creation

section

nation

action

lotion

decision

explosion

vision

division

invasion

REVIEW

INSTRUCTIONS:

Write the words below in the correct columns.

SCOUR, SOUR, COUNT, FOUR, COURT, SOURCE,
MOUSE, ROUND, POUR, TOUR.

your

house

TION / SION

Name

INSTRUCTIONS:
Write the sentence in your best handwriting.

The mouse ran in the house to pounce on the snout of the hound.

REVIEW

INSTRUCTIONS:
Write a word on each line to finish the sentence.
Choose from the following list:
BED, TOP, ROPE, CAKE, PIG, CUP, BAT, FLUTE

A word with a short a is _____ .

A word with a short e is _____ .

A word with a short i is _____ .

A word with a short o is _____ .

A word with a short u is _____ .

A word with a long a is _____ .

A word with a long o is _____ .

A word with a long u is _____ .

REVIEW

INSTRUCTIONS:

The animal friends have gone sailing! Color in the picture following the instructions below.

Color the cat orange.
Color the pig pink.
Color the horse brown.
Color the frog green.
Color the butterfly purple.

TION / SION

INSTRUCTIONS:
Underline all the TION and SION syllables at the end of
the words. Clap out the beats for the syllables and write in
the numbers over the vowels. Then read each word.

starvation

invention

reflection

determination

generation

occupation

imagination

qualification

innovation

education

transportation

separation

TION / SION

INSTRUCTIONS:
Underline all the TION and SION syllables at the end of the words. Clap out the beats for the syllables and write in the numbers over the vowels. Then read each word.

correction   interruption

ignition   protection

duration   foundation

translation   information

television   connection

expression   celebration

MOON MISSION

INSTRUCTIONS:

Blast off to the moon with your own rocket! Copy and cut out the templates below on thick, colored paper. Use markers to decorate a paper towel roll and the cut out templates before any gluing is done. Overlap A and B on the cone piece and glue the edge. Attach side pieces and cone piece to a paper towel roll. Students may make tissue paper flames for under the rocket.

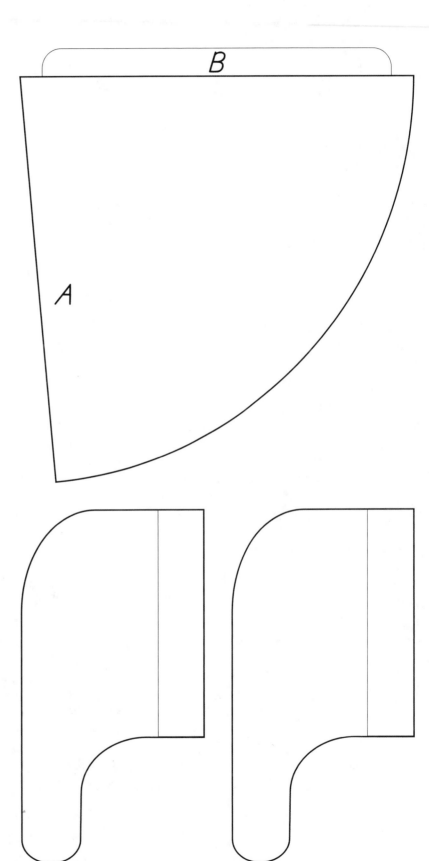

MOON MISSION

Name   *Comprehension*

INSTRUCTIONS:
Cut out the event strips and the timeline strip. Glue the timeline strip to another sheet of 8.5" x 11" paper. Arrange the event strips in the order in which they occured. Glue the event strips to where they belong on the timeline.

1961

1961

July 16, 1969
July 20, 1969

The Eagle lands on the moon.

Three astronauts die
in an explosion

President John Kennedy challenges
America to put a man on the moon.

Apollo 11 lifts off the earth.

Alan Shepard was the first
American in space.

SPELLING TEST 10

1.

2.

3.

4.

5.

6.

7.

8.

9.

10.

Ph

Name

Worksheet 141A

Seeing

INSTRUCTIONS:
PH has the sound of F. Circle the PH in the words below.

phone	phrase
pharaoh	orphan
telephone	telegraph
prophet	pamphlet
elephant	nephew

Ph

Name

Hearing

INSTRUCTIONS:
Circle the boxes purple that have pictures that have the sound of F made by the PH letter combination.

Ph

INSTRUCTIONS:
Read up and down the word columns.

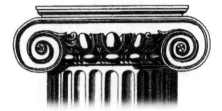

prophet	photo	Special Exhibit:
pharoah	phrase	shepherd
emphatic	emphasis	
physical	elephant	
philosopher	orphan	

Ph

INSTRUCTIONS:
Match the words on the left to the correct picture on the right. There are more words than pictures.

elephant

glacier

pharaoh

telephone

phonograph

social

photo

physician

trophy

ancient

Name

INSTRUCTIONS:
Circle the ED in the words below.

tast(ed)   acted

seated   sounded

started   folded

wanted   added

painted   wasted

listed   blasted

If ED is added to a word that ends in D or T the ED sound is heard. If the word ends in silent E preceeded by a D or T the sound of ED is heard. Otherwise ED at the end of a word says D.

ed

INSTRUCTIONS:
Read up and down the word columns.

ED sound

*Words that end in D or T or a
silent E preceeded by a D or T.*

seat
seated
end
ended
trade
traded
sound
sounded
start
started

D sound

name
named
play
played
turn
turned
save
saved
join
joined

ed

INSTRUCTIONS:
Match the words on the left to their correct ED form on
the right.

call	rained
form	formed
play	sounded
rain	noted
rest	acted
note	called
act	rested
sound	played

ed

INSTRUCTIONS:
Read up and down the word columns.

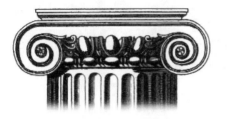  

reach   jump   bake

reached   jumped   baked

wish   camp   look

wished   camped   looked

ed

INSTRUCTIONS:
Read up and down the word columns.

beard
bearded

carpet
carpeted

button
buttoned

rag
ragged

butter
buttered

fence
fenced

curse
cursed

braid
braided

paint
painted

ed

Name

INSTRUCTIONS:
Write the sentence in your best handwriting.

The pharaoh photographed the elephant.

Name

PH / ED

INSTRUCTIONS:
Circle the word that completes each sentence.

1. Egypt was ruled by a boy _____
   named Tutankamen.

    PHARAOH   TELEPHONE   PHRASE

2. My father _____ corn, peas, and potatoes
   in our garden.

    SOUNDED   PLANTED   TRUSTED

3. Jon talked to his buddy on the _____ .

    PHAROAH   TELEPHONE   ELEPHANT

4. Sue, Jim and Parker _____ on the playground.

    PLAYED   SEATED   NAMED

5. The boys _____ baseball cards.

    BAKED   CAMPED   TRADED

6. The _____ at the zoo ate a ton of hay.

    ELEPHANTS   TELEGRAPH   PAMPHLET

7. My mother _____ a cake for supper.

    BAKED   HATCHED   ROPED

8. Kathy _____ Emily for the nice gift.

    LOOKED   SHOUTED   THANKED

Spelling List 11

INSTRUCTIONS:
Copy the PH/ED words below.

1. photo
2. prophet
3. telephone
4. phrase

5. elephant
6. wanted
7. saved

8. started
9. ended
10. traded

1.

2.

3.

4.

5.

6.

7.

8.

9.

10.

ph

INSTRUCTIONS:
Read up and down the word columns.

some	iron	bearded
love	Pharoah	stature
give	ragged	Hebrew
have	shepherd	cursed
one	cawed	decipher
won	people	precious
plague	physical	
guess	hour	

ph

INSTRUCTIONS:
Read up and down the word columns.

quothe	philosopher	appointed
dreary	chime	phase
ponder	emphasis	dread
weary	phony	perished
emphatic	finest	nevermore
reasonable	orphan	
dramatic	foe	
mere	wrath	

420

QUOTHE THE
PROPHET

INSTRUCTIONS:
In the story most of the sentences rhyme. Read the sentence from the story and write in the blank the word that completes the sentence. Remember, it must rhyme. You may use the story itself to help you.

1. But that prophet cawed like a

_____, "Thus says the

Lord, 'Let My people go.'"

2. They do physical work all across

my land. There was no burning

bush out in the _____.

3. You see, the Lord I do not know.

Do you have a clear

_____?

4. I had to make him go away, to

make him see the slaves must

_____.

5. You had better flee, you better

run or I'll make an orphan of your

_____.

6. He knew no fear at least of me;

God told him his people would be

_____.

7. At least that is what he claims,

but I think he is lacking

_____.

8. He wore me down and drove me

bats; he made it rain frogs and

_____.

9. For before I could even draw my

breath the God of Moses plagued

with _____.

10. He sets them free, slaves never-

more, if they had lamb's blood

upon their _____.

11. And He will bear an iron rod,

for He is Lord, the Son of

_____.

QUOTHE THE
PROPHET

INSTRUCTIONS:
Pharaoh and the plagues mobile. Color each picture in,
cut out then tie each circle from a coat hanger using
fishing gline.

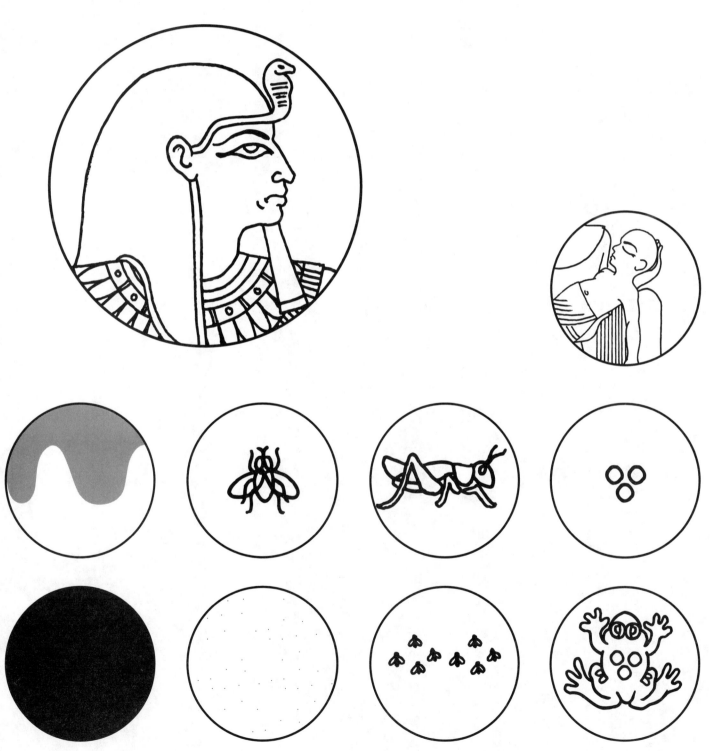

QUOTHE THE
PROPHET

Name

INSTRUCTIONS:
Write the sentence in your best handwriting.

Thus says the Lord, let my people go.

QUOTHE THE
PROPHET

INSTRUCTIONS:
Circle the best answer.

1. Who asked that his people
   be let go?

   PHARAOH

   MOSES

   ABRAHAM

2. Why did Pharaoh want to keep
   the Hebrews?

   THEY DID HIS WORK.

   THEY WERE HIS BUDDIES.

   HE LOVED GOD.

3. Pharaoh said he was strong
   like what?

   A LION

   A BEAR

   AN ELEPHANT

4. Which word was used in the story
   to describe Moses?

   ATHLETIC

   FAT

   BEARDED

5. Which of the following was
   NOT a plague sent by God?

   DARKNESS

   WORMS

   FLIES

6. What happened to
   Pharaoh's son?

   HE BECAME A HEBREW.

   HE BECAME THE NEW PHARAOH.

   HE DIED.

7. How were the Hebrews saved
   from the plague of death?

   THEY PUT LAMB'S BLOOD ON
   THEIR DOORS.

   THEY HID IN CHURCH.

   THEY SACRIFICED AN OX.

8. Whom did God send to release
   His people?

   JUDAS

   HIS SON

   MARY

INSTRUCTIONS:
Read up and down the word columns.

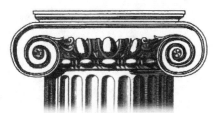

wielded	clan	collapsed
kilt	pirate	dazed
tromped	protector	finally
toil	foil	overtook
daughter	terrified	wee
thatched	hulk	aye
Duke	cleave	plundered
lust	hilt	drab
especially	chink	

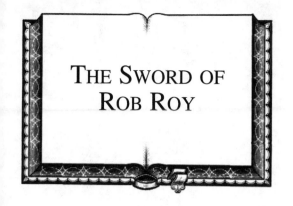

THE SWORD OF
ROB ROY

Name

INSTRUCTIONS:
In the following sentences, one word is not correct. Cross
off the wrong word and above it write the word that makes
the sentence true.

1. A boy was staring at a spear behind the glass box.

2. Rob Roy lived in Ireland.

3. Rob Roy was a carpenter.

4. The King wanted to take Rob Roy's land.

5. Rob Roy was thrown in the jail, so another man could take his land.

6. Rob Roy escaped from the Duke and ran off to hide in a cave.

7. Many priests came to join Rob Roy.

8. Rob Roy jumped out at the men from behind rocks.

9. With a club, a huge man came at Rob Roy.

10. Rob Roy stabbed the Duke with his sword.

11. Everyone praised Rob Roy for his victory.

THE SWORD OF ROB ROY

Name

INSTRUCTIONS:
Complete the crossword puzzle.

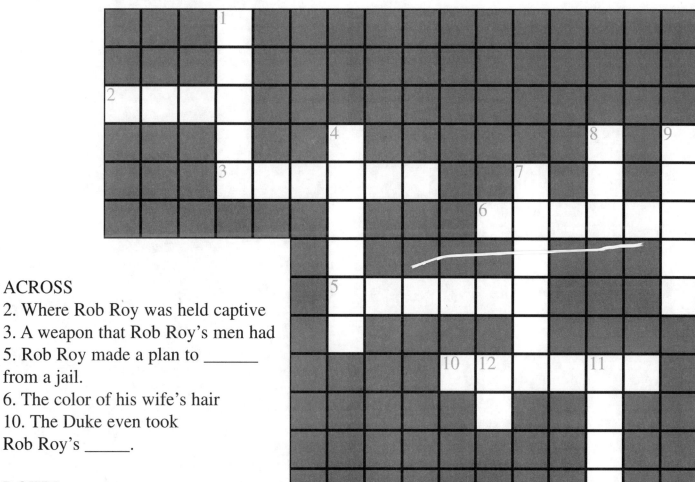

ACROSS

2. Where Rob Roy was held captive
3. A weapon that Rob Roy's men had
5. Rob Roy made a plan to _____ from a jail.
6. The color of his wife's hair
10. The Duke even took Rob Roy's _____.

DOWN

1. What brave men in Scotland wore
4. Rob Roy's job
7. Where the Duke's men attacked Rob Roy and his men
8. Who helped Rob Roy and his men win?
9. What the Duke took from Rob Roy
11. The Duke also took Rob Roy's _____.
12. The big warrior came at Rob Roy with an _____.

SPELLING TEST 11

1.

2.

3.

4.

5.

6.

7.

8.

9.

10.

REVIEW

INSTRUCTIONS:
Fill in the missing letter group.
SH, CH, TH, WH, TCH

__ess wi___ __ale

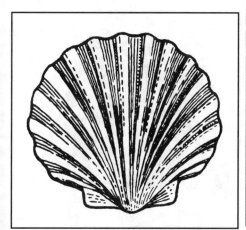  

__ell __umb __oe

439

Name

REVIEW

INSTRUCTIONS:
Fill in the letter group.
ING, ANG, ONG

h___er   r___   l___

s___   k___   sw___

Name _____

REVIEW

INSTRUCTIONS:
Fill in the missing letter group.
CR, FL, TR, SL, FR, DR

 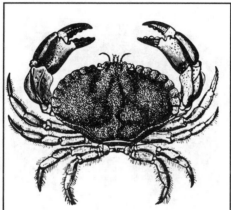 

__og   __ab   __ed

__ag   __ain   __um

Name

REVIEW

INSTRUCTIONS:
Fill in the missing letter groups.
SK, MP, NK, ST, NK, RK

wi__   che__   sta__

a__   si__   ma__

CAUGHT IN
SMILES

_____
Name

INSTRUCTIONS:
Fill in the blanks in the answers below.

1. What is the title of this story?

   The title of the story is _____.

2. Who is the author of this story?

   The author is _____

3. Where does this story take place?

   This story takes place in _____.

4. Name three characters in this story.

   Three characters are_____.

5. Who was a wicked character?

   A wicked character was _____.

6. Describe one character other than the wicked one.

   _____ was _____.

7. What was a problem that Jeanne had?

   Jeanne's problem was that _____.

CAUGHT IN
SMILES

INSTRUCTIONS:
Cut out the pictures and glue them in order in which they happened on another sheet of paper.

CAUGHT IN
SMILES

INSTRUCTIONS:
Fill in the blanks below.

1. What did Henry rise to be?

   In the end, Henry did rise to be _____.

2. How did Jeanne, Henry, and her men escape?

   Jeanne, Henry, and her men played as if they _____.

3. How did Catherine treat Jeanne?

   Catherine hugged and kissed Jeanne and gave her

   _____.

4. What did the boys let Henry win?

   The boys let Henry win _____.

5. How old was Henry when he was brought to Paris?

   Henry was less than _____.

CAUGHT IN
SMILES

INSTRUCTIONS:
Fill in the answers below.

1. What did the Queen Mother break by throwing it at the wall?

_____

_____

_____

2. Of what land was Catherine queen?

_____

_____

_____

3. Why was Henry taken to Paris?

_____

_____

_____

4. Name two ways in which Catherine tried to spoil Henry.

_____

_____

_____

5. How did Jeanne try to train Henry?

_____

_____

_____

CAUGHT IN
SMILES

INSTRUCTIONS:
People during the time of Henry and Catherine wore different clothes than we do today. Photocopy the figures below on card stock then color a royal outfit. Glue a photo of your face in the space provided and cut out the figure.

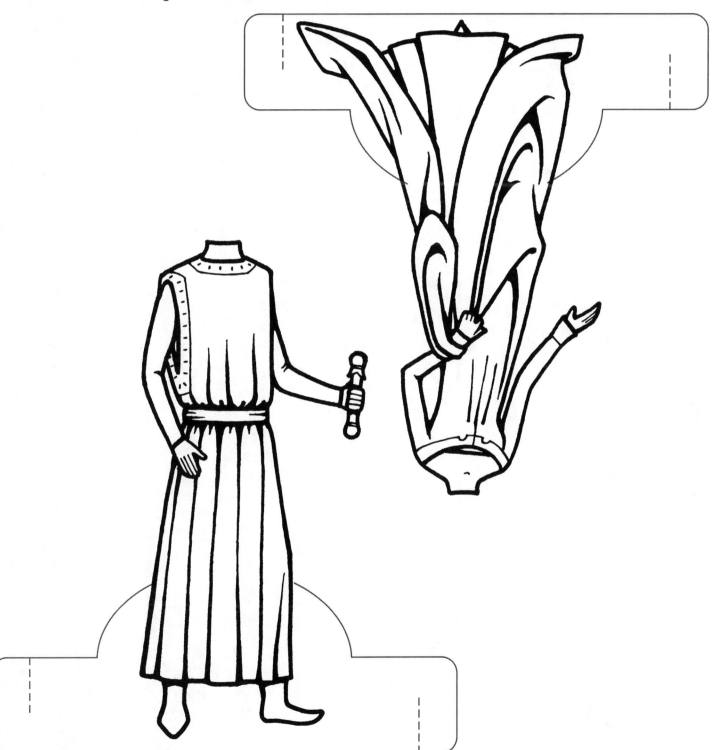

REVIEW

INSTRUCTIONS:
Write out the entire alphabet including both upper and lower case letters.

1.

2.

3.

4.

5.

6.

7.

8.

9.

10.

11.

12.

13.

14.

15.

16.

17.

18.

19.

20.

21.

22.

23.

24.

25.

26.

Name   *Hearing*

INSTRUCTIONS:
Color the boxes brown that have pictures that have the sound of OU or OW as in *out*.

Name

Hearing
Writing

REVIEW

INSTRUCTIONS:
Fill in the missing long vowel.

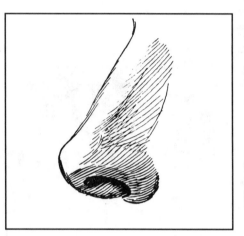

d_me   v_se   n_se

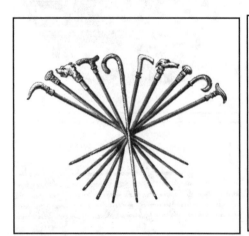

c_nes   gl_be   t_ger

Name

INSTRUCTIONS:
Match the words to the correct picture.

bear

sheep

sailboat

deer

chair

owl

moose

tree

thimble

wheat

Name

REVIEW

INSTRUCTIONS:
Color the boxes green that have pictures that have the sound of OO as in *moon* and the boxes red that have the sound of OO as in *cook*.

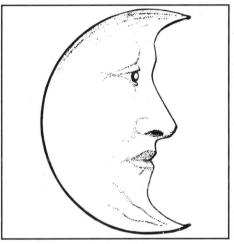

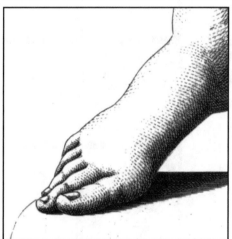

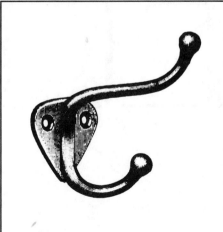

Name

Hearing
Seeing

REVIEW

INSTRUCTIONS:
Color the squares yellow that have vowels in them and red the squares containing consonants.

A	B	C	D	E	F
G	H	I	J	K	L
M	N	O	P	Q	R
S	T	U	V	W	X
Y	Z				

REVIEW

INSTRUCTIONS:
Color the silent partner in each word red.

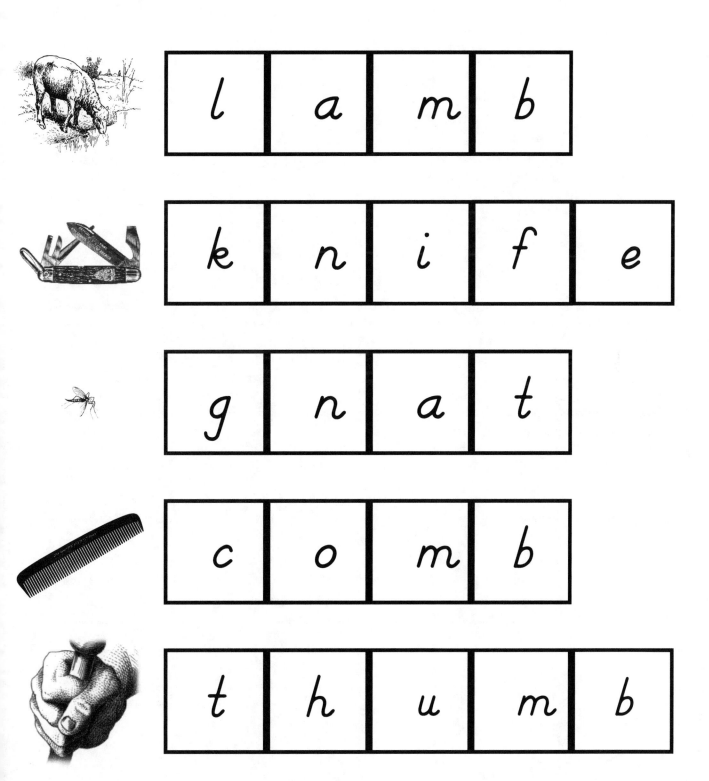

| l | a | m | b |

| k | n | i | f | e |

| g | n | a | t |

| c | o | m | b |

| t | h | u | m | b |

FATHERS' FAITH

INSTRUCTIONS:
Fill in the blanks in the answers below.

1. What is the title of this story?

The title is _____.

2. Who are the authors of this story?

The authors _____.

3. Who is the illustrator of this story?

The illustrator _____.

4. Where are the father and son in this story?

The father _____.

5. Name the son in the story.

The son _____.

6. Name two people about whom father told stories.

Two people _____.

7. What is one problem that Davis has?

One problem _____

_____.

8. What is one thing that the boy pretended to do or be?

Davis pretended _____.

9. Which of the Church Fathers that father told about was your favorite?

_____.

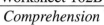

FATHERS' FAITH

INSTRUCTIONS:
Fill in the blanks in the answers below.

1. How did Davis try to find where he should look on the direction sheet?

    Davis tried to find where to look by _____.

2. Who was Augustine's mother?

    Augustine's _____.

3. What book did Augustine open up to read?

    Augustine _____.

4. What happened when Davis tried to chop down the tree?

    When Davis tried to chop down the tree _____

    _____.

5. To what people did Boniface preach?

    Boniface_____.

6. What was made with the wood from the oak tree that the Germans worshipped?

    The wood from the oak tree _____.

7. What was Chrysostom's nickname?

    Chrysostom's _____.

8. What did the emperor do instead of the festival that he promised?

    The emperor _____.

9. What did Ambrose do when the Emperor came to his church?

    Ambose _____.

FATHERS' FAITH

INSTRUCTIONS:
Cut out the name plates on the left and run glue along three sides of each strip then place on another piece of paper to create pockets. Then cut out the sentence strips and place each sentence in the correct pocket. You may use the story to help you to remember.

Augustine

Boniface

Chrysostom

Ambrose

He chopped down a tree that pagans worshipped.

He was named Golden Mouth.

His mother's name was Monica.

He preached to the Germans.

His sermons angered the royals.

Led the emperor to repentance.

He used to be a pagan teacher.

He was from Milan.

He opened up the Bible and the part he read made him a Christian.

He left the city to avoid fighting.

He would not let the emperor come in his church.

He had an oak tree made into a church.

461

FATHERS' FAITH

INSTRUCTIONS:
Write a complete sentence to answer these questions.

1. What was Davis trying to do while Father was off fishing?

_____

_____

2. Whom did Monica pray for each day?

_____

_____

3. What was Davis to do while Father was preparing the fish?

_____

_____

4. What did the German's worship?

_____

_____

5. What did Boniface begin to do that made the Germans angry?

_____

_____

FATHERS' FAITH

INSTRUCTIONS:
Write a complete sentence to answer these questions.

6. Why was Chrysostom called 'The Golden Mouth'?

_____

_____

_____

7. What did Chrysostom do so that the people would not lose their
   lives fighting the emperor?

_____

_____

_____

8. What did the emperor in Ambrose's time say that he was going to do
   to show that he had forgiven the people?

_____

_____

_____

9. What did Ambrose do when the emperor came to his church?

_____

_____

_____

FATHERS' FAITH

INSTRUCTIONS:
Make a diorama of the camping scene from this story.

Name

REVIEW

INSTRUCTIONS:
Match the printed upper case letter to the lower case manuscript letter.

A
B
C
D
E
F
G
H
I
J
K
L
M
N
O
P
Q
R
S
T
U
V
W
X
Y
Z

e
r
t
y
h
b
u
i
a
o
p
l
k
j
g
f
d
s
q
z
x
c
v
w
n
m

TEST

I N S T R U C T I O N S
Circle the correct answer.

knot
coat

glut
goose

trophy
trump

ringer
rooster

foam
phone

crown
croon

cow
cud

flog
flower

hope
hook

huff
house

car
chair

not
note

face
faucet

sell
seal

judge
jump

hat
hate

bird
burn

crawl
crab

bait
badge

cage
cape

price
prince

mate
mice

carpet
castle

camp
comb

TEST

INSTRUCTIONS
Circle the correct answer.

The elephant searched
for a peanut.

The carriage was stuck
in the mud.

The boy was drumming
on his way to the train.

The judge read what was
written on the paper.

The thin man cleaned
the dirty window.

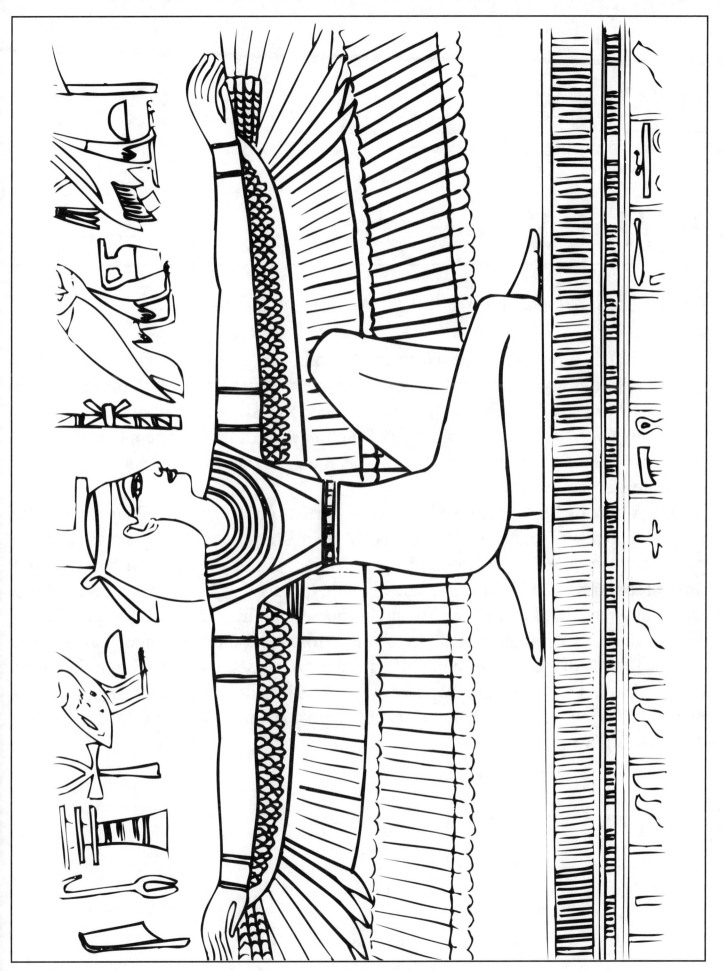

ing/ang/ong
wings

Isis Extends Winged Arms/Seti I Grave, Egypt (c.1300 B.C.)

The ancient Egyptians believed in many gods and goddesses who weren't real gods at all. The Egyptians didn't know about the one true God or his son Jesus. One of their favorite goddesses was Isis (pronounced *eye-sis*). In their stories about the gods, Isis was the wife of Osiris, king of the underworld (where people went when they died). The Egyptians worshiped Isis as their "divine mother" and as protector of the dead.

This picture of Isis was carved by Egyptian artists on the grave of Pharoah Seti the First. Seti was the father of Ramses the Second. Ramses who may have been the pharoah during the Exodus when Moses led Israel out of Egypt and across the Red Sea. At that time, God said to Moses, "The Egyptians will know that I am the Lord when they see what I do to Pharoah and his horses and his chariots." Then God parted the waters of the mighty Red Sea so that Moses and the children of Israel could cross safely on dry land. As Pharoah's strong army chased after Israel into the midst of the sea, God sent the giant walls of water crashing down upon the Egyptian soldiers—killing them all. Then the people of Egypt saw how false and weak their own "gods" really were.

Blends

sleep

Boy Sleeping in the Hay by Albert Anker (1831–1910)

When Albert Anker was a young boy in the village of Anet, Switzerland, he may have taken a nap or two in the hay of a neighbor's barn. And when he grew up and painted peaceful scenes like this one, he may have wished he was young again—with time to do nothing but lie down in the hay and fall asleep.

When Anker was still a young man, he went to Paris to study art. While there, he developed his own special style of portrait and figure painting and was soon earning a living selling his art. Everyone liked his work because he painted scenes of everyday life that people were familiar with.

When Anker was 31 years old, he married Anna Rüefli. They had four children: Louise, Marie, Maurice and Cécile. Anker spent his summers in his hometown of Anet, but he lived in Paris in the winters. He had an art studio there.

He often used his neighbors as models for his paintings. Perhaps the boy in this painting was a boy next door—or maybe even his own son Maurice. Would you like to kick off your shoes and lie down in the hay to take a nap while someone paints a picture of you? Sounds like a nice relaxing job to have, doesn't it?

+r
birds

Transept Pavement, Heptapegon/Israel

How many birds can you name?

How many birds do you know when you see them?

Have you ever seen an oriole? A bald eagle? A penguin? A chickadee?

Do you know that an ostrich is a bird that can't fly?

Do you know that a rooster is a feathered "alarm clock" that will crow good and loud every morning when the sun comes up?

Do you know that a tiny hummingbird can stand still in the air while it beats its wings, and then zoom away so fast that you can hardly see it fly?

Have you ever heard the song of the wood thrush? The sad cry of the mourning dove? The bright chirping of the robin?

But what kind of birds are these that you see here on the Transept Pavement mosaic? Their heads look like ducks or geese, but see how long their legs are? They must be water birds of some kind, perhaps herons or storks. These birds are made out of colored tile. They won't be singing or flying any time soon.

The use of colored tile has a long history in the art of the Middle East, going back to the Babylonians. After a period of neglect, the art style of mosaics was revived in the ninth century. Imagine trying to make a picture out of little bits of colored pottery!

Long Vowels

pipe

Still Life with Pipe and Tobacco (detail) by William Michael Harnett (1848–1892)

Get an armful of your favorite toys and dump them on the kitchen table. Arrange them in a way that makes them still look like they were dumped there but that *also* looks somehow interesting and organized. Then get out your crayons and draw a picture of your pile of toys. When you're done, you will have drawn what artists call "still-life." A still-life is a picture of objects that are just "sitting there." They might be toys on a table, flowers in a vase, fruit in a bowl, or things like the pipe and the can of tobacco shown here.

William Michael Harnett was a master painter of realistic still-life. His paintings looked so real that they were almost like a photo would look today—only better. They looked 3-D (three-dimensional). You felt like you could reach out and touch— or even pick up—the objects in his painting. Many of his still-lifes used objects to tell stories—stories with paint instead of words.

Harnett was born in Ireland in 1838 and came to America (to Philadelphia, Pennsylvania) as a baby. When he was a young man he went to New York City to study painting at an art school. He painted many still-lifes here in America and then traveled to Europe where his artwork became very popular in Germany.

ai/ay

sail

Breezing Up by Winslow Homer (1836–1910)

Have you ever been to the seashore? Have you ever been out on the ocean in a boat or a ship? Isn't the ocean big? Doesn't it look like it goes on and on forever? How would you like to be out there in those big waves in a little boat with just a sail on it? No motor. No oars to row. Just a sail to catch the wind and move you through the water wherever you want to go.

Winslow Homer lived most of his life near the ocean. He was born in 1836 in Boston, where the harbor was always filled with ships that were coming and going. He lived in New York City for awhile too—another city by the sea. There he drew many pictures for a magazine called *Harper's Weekly*. He also started painting at that time—mostly scenes of farms and country life.

Then he traveled to Paris and then to a seacoast town in England where he was once again fascinated by the sea. When he came back to America, he moved to Prout's Neck on the coast of Maine where he painted and lived for the rest of his life. But he continued to travel to many other places—like Florida and Bermuda and Nassau—where the ocean waves rose and fell and the tide rolled out and then it came back in. Though Homer painted many realistic scenes of everyday life, most of his paintings were "soaked" with the sea.

ee/ea

tree

Apollo and Daphne by Pollaiuolo (Antonio Pollaiuolo, 1431?–1498; Piero Pollaiuolo, 1443–1496)

The two Italian Pollaiuolo (pronounced *po lee WO lo*) brothers, Antonio and Piero, worked together on almost everything they did. And they did a lot. They were statue makers, painters, engravers and goldsmiths. They owned a busy artist's workshop in Florence and always signed their work with one name: Pollaiuolo. Antonio was a better artist than Piero, but together they created many beautiful works of art.

Their work illustrated many stories and themes from the Bible and Christian history, as well as from the old stories of the Greek and Roman gods.

Apollo and Daphne illustrates an old Greek legend. Apollo was the son of the Greek god Zeus, king of the gods. Apollo fell in love with a mountain nymph named Daphne. But she did not love him—and so she ran away from him. While Apollo was chasing her, she cried out to her father, a river god who lived in the river nearby. He heard her, and turned her into a laurel tree so that Apollo could not have her. The son of Zeus was very sorry, and he promised that from then on all laurel trees would be forever green. And then he made a wreath of laurel to wear always.

OO
book

Rembrandt's Mother by Gerard Dou (1613–1675)

Gerard Dou was a very popular artist who liked to paint musicians and other people doing everyday things. He also painted many hermits (people who lived alone in order to spend a lot of time praying to God). He became famous for painting night scenes lit by candelight.

Dou's father painted on glass, and that is where Gerard first became interested in painting. But his real education in painting began when he was about 15 years old. It was then that he started working in the studio of another young artist named Rembrandt. Today Rembrandt is more famous than Dou, but when Dou was alive he was more famous than Rembrandt. And because everybody wanted a painting by Dou, he also became very rich.

His painting of Rembrandt's mother is called a *portrait*. A portrait is a picture that looks just like someone, and it is usually of a person's face. When Dou made this picture of Rembrandt's mother, cameras and photographs had not yet been invented. So the only way to make a color portrait was to sit somebody down and paint a picture of their face. Dou was very good at portraits, but *very slow*. So not many people came to him to have their portraits made. They didn't want to have to sit there all day long!

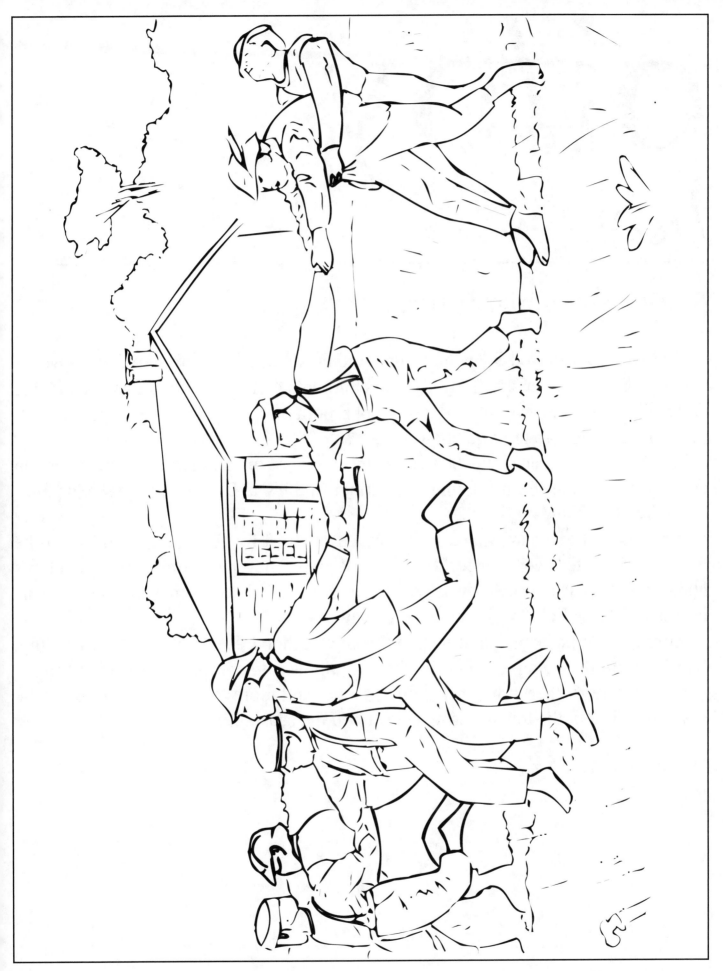

oi/oy
boy

Snap the Whip by Winslow Homer (1836–1910)

Have you ever played Snap the Whip—either running in a yard like these boys, or skating on ice or roller skates? It's an old children's game—like Red Rover and Hide and Seek. If you've never played it, ask your mom or dad—or better yet, your grand-mom or grandad—to tell you about it.

Winslow Homer, the man who painted this scene of fun and play, was an American artist who is famous for his dramatic paintings of the sea. But he also drew and painted many other things.

When he was a young man, he illustrated pictures for magazines. And when he was 25 he started working for *Harper's Weekly*. They paid him to draw pictures about the Civil War—which was being fought at that time. Homer traveled to war-camps and battlefields, drawing what he saw.

After the war he began painting pictures of childhood. He painted children sailing, fishing, farming, going to school in the schoolhouse—and playing Snap the Whip.

Later in life Homer turned his attention more and more to painting pictures of the sea and of life in the towns and villages upon the seashore.

ou/ow

crown

Presentation of Crowns (detail from the *Trés Riches Heures*) by the Limbourg Brothers (c. 1370–1416)

Three brothers, Pol, Hennequin and Herman Limbourg worked together to create a masterpiece of of the fifteenth century. They made the Book of Hours for the Duke Jean de Berry. Berry paid the Limbourgs a lot of money to paint the pictures for this prayer book—and many other paintings tooThe Duke and his brother the King of France gave the most money at that time in Europe to artists to make beautiful things.

The book Pol, Hennequin and Herman made showed what was happening at each point of the year in the lives of the peasants and the royalty. The brothers used brilliant colors to paint the pictures of everyday life and even used real gold to paint!

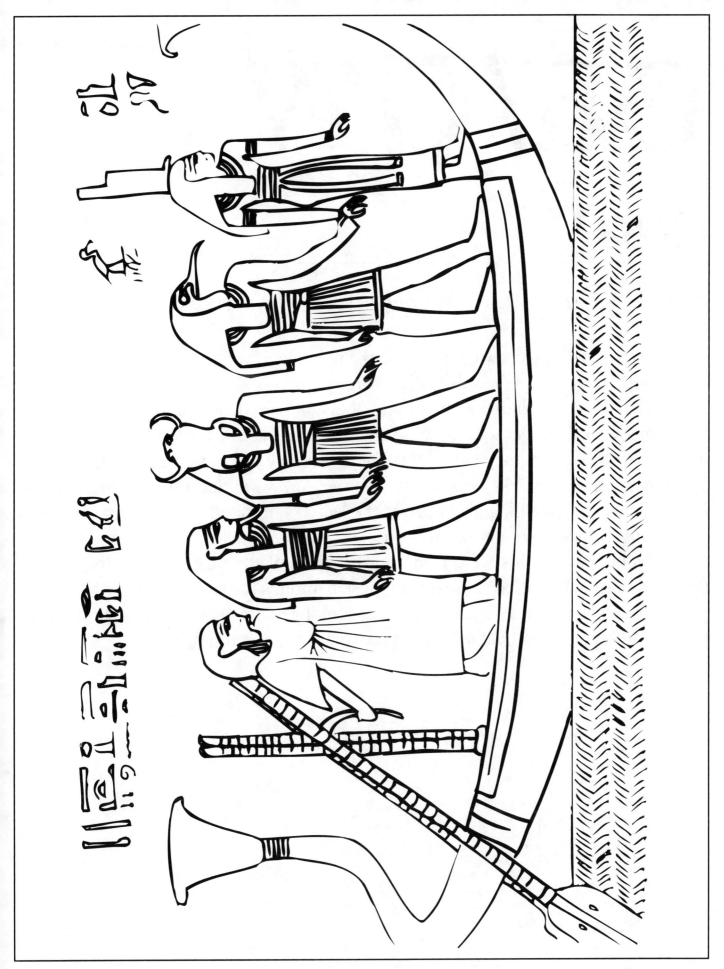

oa/ow

boat

Barge of the Sun on its Night Course/Tomb of Anhurkhawi

When people don't know God, they make up all kinds of things about the universe he created. They imagine gods everywhere: gods of the stars and the sun and the moon and the trees and the rivers and the winds and the seasons. The ancient Egyptians were like that too. They invented their own gods. Their favorite was the god of the sun, whom they called Ra. They probably like him the best because the sun was up there in the sky every day—so big and warm and full of light. High up in the heavens, travelling daily from the eastern horizon to the west, it stared unblinkingly down upon the whole world.

The paintings like this were made on the walls of the places where they buried egyptian kings they called pharoahs. In these paintings the majority of the people are painted sideways but their eyes are painted looking at the viewer. This picture shows the egyptian gods on a boat taking the pharoah to his final judgement.

Soft C

lace

Louis XIII (detail) by Frans Pourbus the Younger (1569–1622)

Frans Pourbus the Younger was a painter. His father, Frans Pourbus the Elder, was also a painter. They lived in Flanders and the Netherlands. Flanders is not a country anymore, but you can see where it used to be if you look at a map of Europe. It was in the north of present-day France and Belgium, with its northern border on the North Sea and its western border on the English Channel.

The Pourbus family painted many pictures from the Bible and about Christianity. They also painted many portraits. One of the portraits painted by Pourbus (the Younger) was of Louis XIII, the king of France.

Louis was only a child when he became king, and so his mother, Marie de Médicis, ruled the country for him until he got older. Marie loved art, and she introduced her nation to the art of two of her neighboring countries: Italy and Flanders.

Louis is not a little boy in his portrait by Pourbus—but he still looks very young to be a king. And look at how fancy his clothing is! How would you like to wear a big lace collar like his?

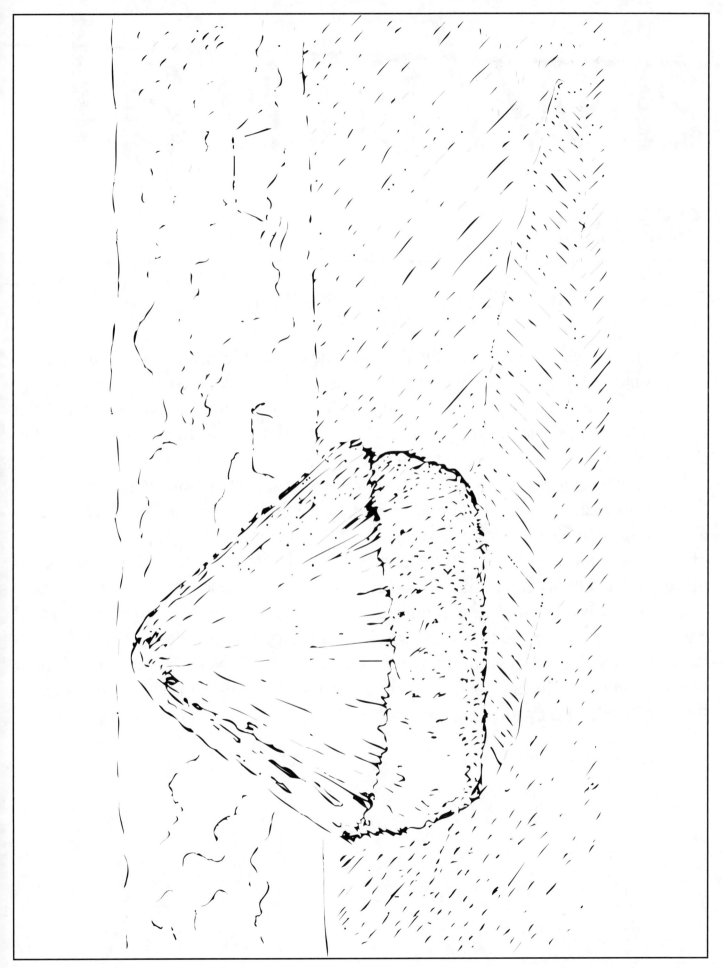

aw/au/al

straw

Haystack in Snow by Claude Monet (1840–1925)

How many ways can you paint one haystack? Claude Monet (pronounced *mo NAY*)painted this one over and over and over again. He wanted to show how one object can look different at different times of the day and in different seasons of the year. So he painted the haystack in the winter, in the summer, in the morning, in the afternoon, at sunset—and many more times.

Monet was an *impressionist*. His art was filled with swirling brushstrokes of color that almost make you blink. The images are sometimes blurry, as if you're looking at them through sleepy eyes or a fogged window. He wanted to paint an *impression* of what things looked like, rather than a realistic picture. He wanted his paintings to make people *feel* instead of think. His artwork created moods instead of told stories.

In 1883, Monet moved to a country home in Giverny, France. There he painted garden scenes. And there he had a waterlilly pond with a footbridge over it.

How many times do you think he painted waterlillies? Well, Monet painted them *so many times* that he once had an artshow with 48 paintings of nothing but waterlillies! And he kept on painting them until he died.

gh
night

Starry Night by Vincent van Gogh (1853–1890)

You have probably seen this painting before. It is the most popular picture of one of the most famous painters of modern art, Vincent van Gogh.

But when Vincent was alive and pouring out his heart and soul on canvas, hardly anybody knew who he was. He was often poor, but in a letter to his brother Theo he once wrote, "I am often as rich…not in money, but rich because I have found in my work something to which I can devote myself with heart and soul, and which gives inspiration and zest to life."

Vincent's paintings were very impressionistic, full of strong, energetic colors and shapes. Before committing himself to a life as a painter, van Gogh, the son of a minister, had been a preacher in the poor coal-mining districts of Belgium. His brother supported Vincent in his painting and they wrote letters to each other. In many of van Gogh's letters he writes lovely descriptions of his choice of paint colors and the feelings he attached to each color. Do different colors mean things to you? What kind of night do the colors make your *Starry Night* picture feel like?

ge/dge

bridge

The Bridge (detail) by Vincent van Gogh (1853–1890)

When Vincent van Gogh was 27 years old (only ten years before his death), he decided to dedicate himself to a life of painting. But he never really made much money with his art. In fact, he only sold one painting in the ten years of his career. "I cannot help it that my pictures do not sell," he wrote in a letter to his brother Theo.

Today he is famous and his paintings are known all around the world. If Vincent van Gogh were here now, he'd be one of the richest painters alive.

But he didn't want money as much as he wanted to paint. He *loved* to paint. To his sister Wil he wrote, "a painter is someone who paints, in the same way that a florist is in reality a person who loves plants and grows them himself."

His first paintings were still-lifes and pictures of country life. They were painted with dark colors and seem sad. But later, just a few years before his death, he moved to the city of Paris and experimented with impressionism. He painted scenes of the city and the suburbs, and his colors became brighter and stronger. His artwork became more alive and expressive. His most famous paintings come from this later time.

tion/sion

adoration

Adoration of the Glorified Christ (detail from the *Trés Riches Heures*) by the Limbourg Brothers (c. 1370–1416)

Today we can go to the store and buy big calendars with pictures of almost anything. There are cat calendars and horse calendars and racecar calendars. There are Dr. Seuss calendars and Winnie the Pooh calendars and American Girl calendars. There are calendars with beautiful photos of mountains and rivers and forests. You can find calendars with pictures by famous artists. Calendars of TV stars and popular musicians and singers. Calendars of your favorite cartoon characters and superheroes. Anything popular *at all* has been made into a calendar.

But did you know that the picture you see here was part of one of the world's first Christian calendars? This painting of Jesus on his throne in heaven is just one of many beautiful illustrations created by the Limbourg brothers for a devotional prayer book called *Trés Riches Heures*. It had prayers and thoughts (and lots of pictures) for different times of the day, each day of the week, and for each month and season of the year.

But *Trés Riches Heures* wasn't available in any store. *There was only one copy!*

ph
pharaoh

Osiris and Atum Seated with Offerings (detail)

The ancient Egyptians believed in a god called Osiris. He ruled the world where people went after they died. The pharoahs (kings) of Egypt believed that they were gods too, and that they were sons of the sun god Ra. But even having a great god like Ra as their father was not enough to get them into paradise. So the Egyptians put pictures on the tombs of the dead to help them on their way.

Then a custom arose called The Book of the Dead, which was a papyrus book (often with pictures) that hadwritings to help insure the soul's entrance into paradise. The Book of the Dead was placed in the coffin with the mummified body of the dead.

In the Book of the Dead there is a story about Osiris. It tells how he sits on his throne in a room with forty-two judges. There he judges the heart of each dead person to see if he has been righteous and true. If he has not, a monster (half crocodile and half hippopotamus) will devour his soul. Another god named Thoth writes down the results on a scroll. We know from the Bible that this is not true.

501

ed
seated

Seated Woman by Mary Stevenson Cassatt (1845–1926)

Sometimes we like to just sit and think, don't we?

What do you suppose the woman is thinking about in *Seated Woman* by Mary Cassatt? Is she listening to a friend? Is she waiting for someone? Is she resting after a long walk?

Mary Cassatt was an American painter and the wealthy daughter of a Philadelphia banker, but when she was 22 years old she moved to France and lived there for the rest of her life. For a long time, her work was very impressionistic, with bright colors and sketchy brushstrokes that created a picture that looks like what we see at a glance.

She was especially famous for her paintings of women and of mothers and their young children.

Some of her later paintings were less impressionistic and more realistic, with black outlines that made them look like illustrations and with flat colors and simple shapes that look like Japanese art.